California Standards
Enrichment Workbook

McDougal Littell

The AMERICANS
Reconstruction to the 21st Century

California Consultant

Neal Cates
Long Beach Unified School District
Lakewood, California

McDougal Littell
A DIVISION OF HOUGHTON MIFFLIN COMPANY

ART CREDITS

xvii Steve Adams/National Geographic Image Collection; **xxii** © 1947 by Herblock in *The Washington Post.* **58** © Bettmann/Corbis; **116** Jay N. "Ding" Darling. © 1937 by the *Des Moines Register* and Tribune Company; **128** © 1947 by Herblock in *The Washington Post.* **158** Tony Auth. © 1974 *The Philadelphia Inquirer.*

ACKNOWLEDGMENTS

History-Social Science Content Standards for California Public Schools reproduced by permission, California Department of Education, CDE Press, 1430 N Street, Suite 3207, Sacramento, CA 95814.

ISBN–13: 978–0–618–57702–6   ISBN–10: 0–618–57702–5

Printed in the United States of America.

10 - DEI - 09 08

Contents

QUICK PREP

CA STANDARDS: REPORTING CLUSTER 1: FOUNDATIONS OF AMERICAN POLITICAL AND SOCIAL THOUGHT

CA STANDARDS: REPORTING CLUSTER 2: INDUSTRIALIZATION AND THE U.S. ROLE AS A WORLD POWER

CA STANDARDS: REPORTING CLUSTER 1: FOUNDATIONS OF AMERICAN POLITICAL AND SOCIAL THOUGHT

CA STANDARDS: REPORTING CLUSTER 2: INDUSTRIALIZATION AND THE U.S. ROLE AS A WORLD POWER

CA STANDARDS: REPORTING CLUSTER 3: UNITED STATES BETWEEN THE WORLD WARS

CA STANDARDS: REPORTING CLUSTER 4: WORLD WAR II AND FOREIGN AFFAIRS

CA STANDARDS: REPORTING CLUSTER 5: POST–WORLD WAR II DOMESTIC ISSUES

CA STANDARDS: REPORTING CLUSTER 4: WORLD WAR II AND FOREIGN AFFAIRS

CA STANDARDS: REPORTING CLUSTER 5: POST–WORLD WAR II DOMESTIC ISSUES

How to Use This Book

The *California Standards Enrichment Workbook* is yours to mark on, to write in, and to make your own. You can use it in class and take it home. The workbook will help you master social studies curriculum, point by point.

For each specific objective or goal in the Grade 11 California Content Standards, your book contains:

- a **Review** page, to summarize the most important content—the issues, ideas, and people behind important events.

- a **Practice** page, that asks you to recall, interpret, analyze, and apply the historical knowledge.

Complete the pages in the order your teacher assigns them. Your teacher will assign pages that match material in your social studies textbook.

You can use the **Quick Prep** section (pages 1–18) to scan important historic eras, leaders, data, and dates, and to look up and learn key terms. The Quick Prep section serves as a handy reference:

- As you work on Review and Practice pages, you can look up key ideas, dates, and definitions.

- The data can help you make inferences, make connections, or answer your own questions as they arise.

- Before a big test, you might use the Quick Prep to review with a peer, a tutor or family member, or on your own.

California History-Social Science Standards

GRADE 11 History-Social Science Content Standards
Reporting Cluster 1: Foundations of American Political and Social Thought

11.1 Students analyze the significant events in the founding of the nation and its attempts to realize the philosophy of government described in the Declaration of Independence.

1. Describe the Enlightenment and the rise of democratic ideas as the context in which the nation was founded.

2. Analyze the ideological origins of the American Revolution, the Founding Fathers' philosophy of divinely-bestowed unalienable rights, the debates on the drafting and ratification of the Constitution, and the addition of the Bill of Rights.

3. Understand the history of the Constitution after 1787 with emphasis on federal versus state authority and growing democratization.

4. Examine the effects of the Civil War and Reconstruction and of the industrial revolution, including demographic shifts and the emergence in the late nineteenth century of the United States as a world power.

11.3 Students analyze the role religion played in the founding of America, its lasting moral, social and political impacts, and issues regarding religious liberty.

1. Describe the contributions of various religious groups to American civic principles and social reform movements (e.g., civil and human rights, individual responsibility and the work ethic, antimonarchy and self-rule, worker protection, family-centered communities).

2. Analyze the great religious revivals and the leaders involved in them, including the First Great Awakening, the Second Great Awakening, the Civil War revivals, the Social Gospel Movement, the rise of Christian liberal theology in the nineteenth century, the impact of the Second Vatican Council, and the rise of Christian fundamentalism in current times.

3. Cite incidences of religious intolerance in the United States (e.g., persecution of Mormons, anti-Catholic sentiment, anti-Semitism).

4. Discuss the expanding religious pluralism in the United States and California that resulted from large-scale immigration in the twentieth century.

5. Describe the principles of religious liberty found in the Establishment and Free Exercise clauses of the First Amendment, including the debate on the issue of separation of church and state.

GRADE 11 History-Social Science Content Standards
Reporting Cluster 2: Industrialization and the U.S. Role as a World Power

11.2 Students analyze the relationships among the rise of industrialization, large-scale rural-to-urban migration, and massive immigration from Southern and Eastern Europe.

1. Know the effects of industrialization on living and working conditions, including the portrayal of working conditions and food safety in Upton Sinclair's *The Jungle*.

2. Describe the changing landscape, including the growth of cities linked by industry and trade, and the development of cities divided according to race, ethnicity, and class.

3. Trace the effect of the Americanization movement.

4. Analyze the effect of urban political machines and responses to them by immigrants and middle-class reformers.

5. Discuss corporate mergers that produced trusts and cartels and the economic and political policies of industrial leaders.

6. Trace the economic development of the United States and its emergence as a major industrial power, including its gains from trade and advantages of its physical geography.

7. Analyze the similarities and differences between the ideologies of Social Darwinism and Social Gospel (e.g., using biographies of William Graham Sumner, Billy Sunday, Dwight L. Moody).

8. Examine the effect of political programs and activities of Populists.

9. Examine the effect of political programs and activities of the Progressives (e.g., federal regulation of railroad transport, Children's Bureau, the Sixteenth Amendment, Theodore Roosevelt, Hiram Johnson).

11.4 Students trace the rise of the United States to its role as a world power in the twentieth century.

1. List the purpose and the effects of the Open Door policy.

2. Describe the Spanish-American War and U.S. expansion in the South Pacific.

3. Discuss America's role in the Panama Revolution and the building of the Panama Canal.

4. Explain Theodore Roosevelt's Big Stick diplomacy, William Taft's Dollar Diplomacy, and Woodrow Wilson's Moral Diplomacy, drawing on relevant speeches.

5. Analyze the political, economic, and social ramifications of World War I on the home front.

6. Trace the declining role of Great Britain and the expanding role of the United States in world affairs after World War II.

GRADE 11 History-Social Science Content Standards
Reporting Cluster 3: United States Between the World Wars

11.5 Students analyze the major political, social, economic, technological, and cultural developments of the 1920s.

1. Discuss the policies of Warren Harding, Calvin Coolidge, and Herbert Hoover.

2. Analyze the international and domestic events, interests and philosophies that prompted attacks on civil liberties, including the Palmer Raids, Marcus Garvey's "back-to-Africa" movement, the Ku Klux Klan, and immigration quotas and the responses of organizations such as the American Civil Liberties Union, the National Association for the Advancement of Colored People, and the Anti-Defamation League to those attacks.

3. Examine the passage of the Eighteenth Amendment to the Constitution and the Volstead Act (Prohibition).

4. Analyze the passage of the Nineteenth Amendment and the changing role of women in society.

5. Describe the Harlem Renaissance and new trends in literature, music, and art, with special attention to the work of writers (e.g., Zora Neale Hurston, Langston Hughes).

6. Trace the growth and effects of radio and movies and their role in the worldwide diffusion of popular culture.

7. Discuss the rise of mass production techniques, the growth of cities, the impact of new technologies (e.g., the automobile, electricity), and the resulting prosperity and effect on the American landscape.

11.6 Students analyze the different explanations for the Great Depression and how the New Deal fundamentally changed the role of the federal government.

1. Describe the monetary issues of the late nineteenth and early twentieth centuries that gave rise to the establishment of the Federal Reserve and the weaknesses in key sectors of the economy in the late 1920s.

2. Understand the explanations of the principal causes of the Great Depression and the steps taken by the Federal Reserve, Congress, and Presidents Herbert Hoover and Franklin Delano Roosevelt to combat the economic crisis.

3. Discuss the human toll of the Depression, natural disasters, and unwise agricultural practices and their effects on the depopulation of rural regions and on political movements of the
    left and right, with particular attention to the Dust Bowl refugees and their social and economic impacts.

4. Analyze the effects of and the controversies arising from New Deal economic policies and the expanded role of the federal government in society and the economy since the 1930s (e.g., Works Progress Administration, Social Security, National Labor Relations Board, farm programs, regional development policies, and energy development projects such as the Tennessee Valley Authority, California Central Valley Project, and Bonneville Dam).

5. Trace the advances and retreats of organized labor, from the creation f the American Federation of Labor and the Congress of Industrial Organizations to current issues of a post-industrial, multinational economy, including the United Farm Workers in California.

GRADE 11 History-Social Science Content Standards
Reporting Cluster 4: World War II and Foreign Affairs

11.7 Students analyze America's participation in World War II.

1. Examine the origins of American involvement in the war, with an emphasis on the events that precipitated the attack on Pearl Harbor.

2. Explain U.S. and Allied wartime strategy, including the major battles of Midway, Normandy, Iwo Jima, Okinawa, and the Battle of the Bulge.

3. Identify the roles and sacrifices of individual American soldiers, as well as the unique contributions of the special fighting forces (e.g., the Tuskegee Airmen, the 442nd Regimental Combat team, the Navajo Codetalkers).

4. Analyze Roosevelt's foreign policy during World War II (e.g., Four Freedoms speech).

5. Discuss the constitutional issues and impact of events on the U.S. home front, including the internment of Japanese Americans (e.g., Fred Korematsu v. United States of America) and the restrictions on German and Italian resident aliens; the response of the administration to Hitler's atrocities against Jews and other groups; the roles of women in military production; and the roles and growing political demand of African Americans.

6. Describe the major developments in aviation, weaponry, communication, and medicine and the war's impact on the location of American industry and use of resources.

7. Discuss the decision to drop atomic bombs and the consequences of the decision (Hiroshima and Nagasaki).

8. Analyze the effect of massive aid given to western Europe under the Marshall Plan to rebuild itself after the ware and the importance of a rebuilt Europe to the U.S. economy.

11.9 Students analyze U.S. foreign policy since World War II.

1. Discuss the establishment of the United Nations and International Declaration of Human Rights, International Monetary Fund, World Bank, and General Agreement on Tariffs and Trade (GATT0, and their importance in shaping modern Europe and maintaining peace and international order.

2. Understand the role of military alliances, including NATO and SEATO, in deterring communist aggression and maintaining security during the Cold War.

3. Trace the origins and geopolitical consequences (foreign and domestic) of the Cold War and containment policy, including the following:

   - The era of McCarthyism, instances of domestic communism (e.g., Alger Hiss) and blacklisting
   - The Truman Doctrine
   - The Berlin Blockade
   - The Korean War
   - The Bay of Pigs invasion and the Cuban Missile Crisis
   - Atomic Testing in the American West, the "mutual assured destruction" doctrine, and disarmament policies
   - The Vietnam War
   - Latin American policy

4. List the effects of foreign policy on domestic policies and vice versa (e.g., protests during the war in Vietnam, the "nuclear freeze" movement).

5. Analyze the role of the Reagan Administration and other factors in the victory of the West in the Cold War.

6. Describe U.S. Middle East policy and its strategic, political, and economic interests, including those related to the Gulf War.

7. Examine relations between the United States and Mexico in the twentieth century, including key economic, political, immigration, and environmental issues.

GRADE 11 History-Social Science Content Standards
Reporting Cluster 5: Post–World War II Domestic Issues

11.8 Students analyze the economic boom and social transformation of post–World War II in America.

1. Trace the growth of service sector, white collar, and professional sector jobs in business and government.

2. Describe the significance of Mexican immigration and its relationship to the agricultural economy, especially in California.

3. Examine Truman's labor policy and congressional reaction to it.

4. Analyze federal government spending on defense, welfare, interest on the national debt, and federal and state spending on education, including the California Master Plan.

5. Describe the increased powers of the presidency in response to the Great Depression, World War II, and the Cold War.

6. Discuss the diverse environmental regions in North America, their relationship to local economies, and the origins and prospects of environmental problems in those regions.

7. Describe the effects of society and the economy of technological developments since 1945, including the computer revolution, changes in communication, advances in medicine, and improvement in agricultural technology.

8. Discuss forms of popular culture, with emphasis on their origins and geographic diffusion (e.g., jazz and other forms of popular music, professional sports, architectural and artistic styles).

11.10 Students analyze the development of federal civil rights and voting rights.

1. Explain how demands of African Americans helped produce a stimulus for civil rights, including President Roosevelt's ban on racial discrimination in defense industries in 1941, and how African Americans' service in World War II produced a stimulus for President Truman's decision to end segregation in the armed forces in 1948.

2. Examine and analyze the key events, policies, and court cases in the evolution of civil rights, including Dred Scott v. Sandford, Plessy v. Ferguson, Brown v. Board of Education, Regents of the University of California v. Bakke, and California Proposition 209.

3. Describe the collaboration on legal strategy between African American and white civil rights lawyers to end racial segregation in higher education.

4. Examine the roles of civil rights advocates (e.g., Philip Randolph, Martin Luther King, Jr., Malcolm X, Thurgood Marshall, James Farmer, Rosa Parks), including the significance of Martin Luther King, Jr.'s "Letter from Birmingham Jail" and "I Have a Dream" speech.

5. Discussion diffusion of the civil rights movement of African Americans from the churches of the rural South and the urban North, including the resistance to racial desegregation in Little Rock and Birmingham, and how the advances influenced the agendas, strategies, and effectiveness of the quests of American Indians, Asian Americans, and Hispanic Americans for civil rights and equal opportunities.

6. Analyze the passage and effects of civil rights and voting rights legislation (e.g., 1964 Civil Rights Act, Voting Rights Act of 1965) and the Twenty-Fourth Amendment, with an emphasis on equality of access to education and to the political process.

7. Analyze the women's rights movement from the era of Elizabeth Stanton and Susan Anthony and the passage of the Nineteenth Amendment to the movement launched in the 1960s, including differing perspectives on the roles of women.

11.11 Students analyze the major social problems and domestic policy issues in contemporary American society.

1. Discuss the reasons for the nation's changing immigration policy, with emphasis on how the Immigration Act of 1965 and successor acts have transformed American society.

2. Discuss the significant domestic policy speeches of Truman, Eisenhower, Kennedy, Johnson, Nixon, Carter, Reagan, Bush, and Clinton (e.g., with regard to education, civil rights, economic policy, environmental policy).

3. Describe the changing roles of women in society as reflected in the entry of more women into the labor force and the changing family structure.

4. Explain the constitutional crisis originating from the Watergate scandal.

5. Trace the impact of, need for, and controversies associated with environmental conservation, expansion of the national park system, and the development of environmental protection laws, with particular attention to the interaction between environmental protection advocates and property rights advocates.

6. Analyze the persistence of poverty and how different analyses of this issue influence welfare reform, health insurance reform, and other social policies.

7. Explain how the federal, state, and local governments have responded to demographic and social changes such as population shifts to the suburbs, racial concentrations in the cities, Frostbelt-to-Sunbelt migration, international migration, decline of family farms, increases in out-of-wedlock births, and drug abuse.

California History-Social Science Analysis Skills (Grade 11)

Chronological and Spatial Thinking

CST 1   Students compare the present with the past, evaluating the consequences of past events and decisions and determining the lessons that were learned.

CST 2   Students analyze how change happens at different rates at different times; that some aspects can change while other remain the same; and understand that change is complicated and affect not only technology and politics but also values and beliefs.

CST 3   Students use a variety of maps and documents to interpret human movement including major patterns of domestic and international migration, changing environmental preferences and settlement patterns, the frictions that develop between population groups, and the diffusion of ideas, technological innovations, and goods.

CST 4   Students relate current events to the physical and human characteristics of places and regions.

Research, Evidence, and Point of View

REP 1   Students distinguish valid arguments from fallacious arguments in historical interpretations.

REP 2   Students identify bias and prejudice in historical interpretations.

REP 3   Students evaluate major debates among historians concerning alternative interpretations of the past, including an analysis of authors' use of evidence and the distinctions between sound generalizations and misleading oversimplifications.

REP 4   Students construct and test hypotheses; collect, evaluate, and employ information from multiple primary and secondary sources; and apply it in oral and written presentations.

Historical Interpretation

HI 1   Students show the connections, casual and otherwise, between particular historical events and larger social, economic, and political trends and developments.

HI 2   Students recognize the complexity of historical causes and effects, including the limitations of determining cause and effect.

HI 3   Students interpret past events and issues within the context in which an event unfolded rather than solely in terms of present day norms and values.

HI 4   Students understand the meaning, implication, and impact of historical events while recognizing that events could have taken other directions.

HI 5   Students analyze human modifications of landscapes, and examine the resulting environmental policy issues.

HI 6   Students conduct cost/benefit analyses and apply basic economic indicators to analyze the aggregate economic behavior of the U.S. economy.

Quick Prep

This Quick Prep section provides a handy reference to key facts on a variety of topics in American history.

Major Eras of American History

Era and Dates	Description
Pre-European Contact c. 1000 B.C.–1492	Flourishing societies of indigenous peoples live by hunting, farming, fishing, and trading.
Exploration & Colonization 1492–1763	Europeans explore, establish colonies, create conflict with Native Americans; European rivalries continue.
Revolutionary Era 1763–1789	Maturing colonial economies; increasing tension with Great Britain leads to war and independence.
Early Republic 1789–1812	New federal government; first political parties; uncertain international relations; expansion to the Mississippi
Westward Expansion 1812–1846	Growth in transportation and industry; Jacksonian democracy; Manifest Destiny; removal of Native Americans
Antebellum Era 1836–1860	Differences over expansion of slavery leads to increasing sectionalism; conflict with Mexico.
Civil War and Reconstruction 1860–1877	War over states' rights to secede and emancipation; union preserved; voting rights for African Americans
Industrial Age/ Gilded Age 1877–1900	Immigration, industrialization, urbanization Big business, railroads, organized labor, machine politics
Progressive Era 1890–1920	Reform—urban problems; temperance; government and business corruption; women's right to vote.
American Imperialism 1890–1920	America becomes a world power, gains overseas colonies.
World War I 1914–1918	European conflict challenges U.S. policy of neutrality; Allied victory intended to make the world safe for democracy.
Roaring Twenties 1920–1929	Business booms, superficial prosperity; new lifestyles for women; growth of mass media; Red Scare
Great Depression 1929–1941	World trade declines, banks fail, high unemployment, urban and rural poverty; New Deal expands role of federal government.
World War II 1939–1945	Dictators threaten world peace on 2 fronts—Europe and Pacific; mobilizes U.S. economy and industry; U.S. helps win war and becomes a world leader
Cold War 1945–1989	Tension and competition between U.S. and Communist USSR; threat of nuclear war; McCarthyism (1950s)
Postwar Boom 1946–1959	American dream—social conformity, suburban and automobile culture, baby boom, consumerism; TV
New Frontier and Great Society 1960–1968	New leadership, bold ideas, prosperity; space race Johnson's Great Society—social welfare, civil rights
Civil Rights Movement 1954–1968	Nonviolent protest—voting rights, desegregation; federal support vs. states' resistance; Black Power movement and urban riots
Vietnam War Years 1954–1975	Domino theory—contain communism War divides the country—campus protest, draft resistance
Era of Social Change 1960–1975	Women, Latinos, and Native Americans seek equality; Hippie counterculture; "do your own thing"
End of the 20th Century 1970s–1990s	1970s—inflation, energy crisis, environmentalism 1980s—political conservatism, federal deficit 1990s—booming economy, digital revolution, economic globalization

Important Events in American History

Date	Event	Significance
1492	Columbus first lands in America	begins sustained European contact
1607	founding of Jamestown, Va.	first permanent English colony
1620	Pilgrims at Plymouth	beginning of permanent settlement of New England
1754–1763	French and Indian War	Britain ends French presence in the colonies
1775–1783	Revolutionary War	U.S. wins independence from Britain
1776	Declaration of Independence	America breaks with Britain
1781	Articles of Confederation	first attempt at national government
1787	U.S. Constitution signed	federal government established
1793	First textile mill in U.S.	Industrial Revolution comes to America
1803	Louisiana Purchase	doubles the size of the country
1812–1814	War of 1812 with Britain	U.S. maintains independence
1831–1833	Nullification Crisis	South Carolina threatens to secede
1830s	Indian removal—Trail of Tears	Eastern native nations (especially Cherokee) forced west
1837	telegraph invented	long distance communication unites country
1846–1848	War with Mexico	U.S. gains additional territory in the Southwest
1850	Bessemer steel process developed	allows development of railroads, skyscrapers, bridges
1861–1865	Civil War	the Union is preserved and slavery ends
1869	first transcontinental railroad completed	faster travel coast to coast
1876	telephone invented	long distance voice communication
1877	end of Reconstruction	South begins era of segregation
1880	electric light bulb	inexpensive form of light for homes and businesses
1886	American Federation of Labor formed	first effective group of labor unions; still active today as AFL-CIO
1890	Battle of Wounded Knee	end of Indian Wars in the West
1892	Populist Party formed	farmers unite against railroads and big business
April–Aug. 1898	Spanish-American War	U.S. gains an empire in Caribbean and Philippines
1909	NAACP formed	African Americans organize to achieve equality
1910–1920	Great Migration of African Americans	growth of large African-American communities in Northern cities; racial tensions develop
1913	Ford produces one auto every 2 hours	mass production techniques make U.S. world industrial leader
1914	Panama Canal completed	travel between Caribbean and the Pacific eased
1914–1918	World War I	European conflict challenges U.S. neutrality
1917	U.S. enters World War I	tips the balance of power to the Allies; Central Powers defeated
1919	League of Nations chartered	agreement to settle differences without war
1919–1933	Prohibition	established shared popular culture across nation
1920	first commercial radio station	alcoholic beverages banned; flaunting of the law
1920	women get the right to vote	women achieve political equality sought since 1848
1919–1920	Red Scare	fear of Communist takeover of America
1924	immigration quotas set	limits Southern and Eastern Europeans; no Asians
1925	Scopes trial	debate between religion and science over teaching evolution
1927	Lindbergh flies solo across the Atlantic; first commercial air flights	modern age of air travel begins
1929	Stock market crashes	Great Depression begins
1930	major cities connected by paved roads	increased travel by car with greater speed and convenience
1933	New Deal begins	unprecedented expansion of the role of federal government
1933–1936	Dust Bowl	increased poverty; large numbers migrate to California

Date	Event	Significance
Sept. 1939	Hitler invades Poland	World War II begins
Dec. 7, 1941	Japanese attack Pearl Harbor	U.S. enters World War II
1941–1945	U.S. involvement in World War II	U.S. becomes a world power
Feb. 1942	internment of Japanese Americans begins	violation of civil rights
June 1942	Battle of Midway	Japanese fleet decimated; U.S. begins island hopping
June 6, 1944	D-Day	Allies invade Normandy; begin liberation of Europe
Aug. 6 & 9, 1945	atomic bombs devastate Japan	ends World War II; begins nuclear age
1950–1953	Korean War	desire to contain Communism ends in stalemate
1950–1954	McCarthyism	fear of Communism leads to civil rights violations
1950s	TV becomes popular	shared popular culture expands; Americans now watch about 4 hours each day
1951	UNIVAC first computer sold commercially	Computer revolution begins, resulting in widespread personal computer and Internet use
1954–1973	American involvement in Vietnam	longest war in American history divides the nation
1954	*Brown* v. *Board of Education*	Supreme Court mandates school desegregation
1954	polio vaccine introduced	elimination of deadly childhood disease within 20 years
Dec. 1955–Dec.1956	Montgomery bus boycott	first nonviolent civil rights protest
Sept. 1957	USSR launches Sputnik I satellite	begins the space race
Sept.1957	Little Rock (Arkansas) Nine	fight for school desegregation begins
1961	Bay of Pigs invasion in Cuba	failed attempt by U.S. to overthrow Castro
1962	Cuban missile crisis	U.S. and USSR come to brink of nuclear war
1963	March on Washington; King's "I Have a Dream" speech	leads to Civil Rights Act of 1964
Nov. 22, 1963	President Kennedy assassinated	tragedy unites the country in grief
1964	Tonkin Gulf Resolution	begins undeclared war in Vietnam
May 1964	Johnson launches Great Society	war on poverty; support for civil rights
1966	National Organization for Women founded	women unite to achieve equality
1967	race riots in major cities	civil rights movement turns violent
January 1968	Tet offensive	causes moderates to turn against the war in Vietnam
1968	Martin Luther King, Jr. and Robert Kennedy assassinated	sparks national rioting and protest
1969	Neil Armstrong walks on the moon	America wins the space race with USSR
April 22, 1970	first Earth Day	signals growing interest in environmentalism
May 1970	student protestors killed at Kent State	deepens division over the war
1972	Congress passes the Equal Rights Amendment	gender equality; not ratified
Feb. 1972	President Nixon visits China	opens relations closed since 1949
1973	U.S. troops withdraw from Vietnam	war turned over to the Vietnamese
1973	beginning of energy crisis	America's overdependence on Middle Eastern oil
Aug. 1974	Watergate scandal; President Nixon resigns	diminishes faith in government
1975	fall of Saigon	communists rule Vietnam; war spreads throughout SE Asia
Nov. 1979–Jan. 1981	Iran holds 52 Americans hostage	conflict over the shah
1981	Sandra Day O'Connor appointed to Supreme Court	first woman justice
1989–1991	fall of the Berlin Wall; breakup of the Soviet Union	Cold War ends
1990–1991	Persian Gulf War	U.S. supports Kuwait; protects its oil supplies
Dec. 1998–Jan. 1999	President Clinton's impeachment trial	remains in office
Sept 11, 2001	terrorists attack World Trade Center and Pentagon	U.S. begins war on terrorism
March 2003	U.S. invades Iraq	fear of weapons of mass destruction and terrorism; brutal dictator removed

Important Documents in American History

Magna Carta (1215) English agreement that guaranteed certain rights to all Englishmen; influenced the American Bill of Rights' protections of individual rights

English Bill of Rights (1689) English agreement that guaranteed certain rights to all Englishmen; influenced the American Bill of Rights' protections of individual rights

Mayflower Compact (1620) Signed by many Pilgrims on their way to New World; they agreed to create a new government and follow its laws; helped establish the idea of self-government

***Common Sense* (1776)** Influential pamphlet written by Thomas Paine; it urged Americans to declare their independence

Declaration of Independence (July 4, 1776) Written by Thomas Jefferson; announced the separation of the colonies from England

Articles of Confederation (1781–1789) First U.S. government; it was eventually a failure because it created a national government that was too weak

Constitution (written in 1787) Blueprint for the American government

The Federalist Papers (1787–1788) Series of essays about the nature of government by Alexander Hamilton, James Madison, and John Jay; written to help get the Constitution ratified

Bill of Rights (adopted in 1791) First 10 amendments of the Constitution; guarantees individual rights

Monroe Doctrine (1823) Presidential message that said that Europe should not interfere in the affairs of Latin America and the United States would not interfere in European affairs

"South Carolina Exposition and Protest" (1829) Written by John C. Calhoun; outlined the doctrine of nullification, which was a strong statement for states' rights

***The Liberator* (1831–1865)** Newspaper printed by William Lloyd Garrison; most influential antislavery periodical in United States history; it increased sectionalism between the North and South

Emancipation Proclamation (Jan. 1, 1863) Executive order given by Abraham Lincoln; it freed the slaves in the Confederacy

Gettysburg Address (1863) Famous speech given by Abraham Lincoln; it said that the Union was worth fighting for at any cost

Lincoln's Second Inaugural (1865) Lincoln said Civil War was about slavery and that the Union was fighting to end slavery

Bryan's "Cross of Gold" speech" (1896) stated Populist position against gold standard which favored business and bankers; ran for president as Democrat but lost and Populism lost power

Zimmermann Note (1917) telegram from Germany to Mexico offering help in recovering territory in the southwest U.S.; U.S. entered World War I

The Fourteen Points (1918) President Woodrow Wilson's plan for peace after World War I; proposed a League of Nations

Covenant of the League of Nations (1920) established an organization to settle international disputes diplomatically; U.S. never joined; forerunner of the United Nations

Roosevelt's "Four Freedoms" speech (1941) stated hopes for post-war world where all would have freedom of speech and worship and freedom from want and fear; influenced U.N. charter

United Nations Charter (1945) created a new organization of nations dedicated to world peace and international cooperation

Truman Doctrine (1947) U.S. would support free people resisting takeover from hostile forces within or outside of their countries

Marshall Plan (1947) Secretary of state George Marshall's plan to provide aid to help Europe rebuild after World War II

"Letter from the Birmingham Jail" (1963) Martin Luther King, Jr.'s statement of his philosophy of nonviolent protest

"I Have a Dream" speech (1963) Martin Luther King, Jr.'s vision of racial harmony; March on Washington

Pentagon Papers (1971) Defense Department document revealing government's lack of honesty in its communication about Vietnam

Carter's "Moral Equivalent of War" speech (1977) focused attention on U.S. dependence on foreign oil for economic and personal needs; resulted in National Energy Act

Contract with America (1994) Congressman Newt Gingrich's conservative plan for government reform; helped Republicans gain control of Congress

Constitutional Amendments

The first ten amendments were passed in 1791 and are collectively called the Bill of Rights.

1. Five freedoms—**separation of church and state; freedom of speech, press, and assembly; right to petition government** for settlement of a complaint or to make up for wrongdoing
2. Right to bear **arms**
3. **Quartering of troops** prohibited in peacetime without permission
4. No unreasonable **search and seizure**
5. **Rights of accused persons**—capital crimes require Grand Jury indictment; can't be tried twice for the same crime (no double jeopardy); can't be compelled to testify against yourself; can't be deprived of life, liberty, or property without due process of law; owner must be compensated for private property taken for public use
6. Right to **speedy, public trial**
7. Right to **trial by jury** in civil cases
8. **Limits of fines and punishments**—no excessive bail nor cruel or unusual punishment
9. **Rights of the people**—rights stated in the Constitution are not the only rights that people have
10. Powers not delegated to the federal government nor denied to the states by the Constitution are **reserved to the states or the people**
11. **Lawsuits against states (1798)** Federal judicial power does not extend to lawsuits brought against individual states.
12. **Election of executives (1804)** Established procedures for the electoral college to vote for specific candidates for president and vice-president.
13. **Slavery abolished (1865)** Involuntary servitude is illegal except as punishment for a crime.
14. **Civil rights (1868)** All persons born or naturalized in the U.S. are citizens; states may not abridge rights of citizens—equal protection of the law, due process, compensation if the government takes private property. States will lose some representation if they deny the vote to any male citizens. Former Confederate leaders not allowed to hold government positions.
15. **Right to vote (1870)** Voting privileges cannot be denied on the basis of race or previous condition of servitude.
16. **Income tax (1913)** Legalized a direct tax on income and profit, not dependent on population distribution.
17. **Direct election of Senators (1913)** U.S. Senators will be elected by the people, not by state legislatures.
18. **Prohibition (1919)** The manufacture, transportation, or sale of alcoholic beverages is prohibited.
19. **Woman suffrage (1920)** Women gained the right to vote equal to men.
20. **"Lame duck" sessions (1933)** The terms of president and vice-president end on January 20, and of Congress on January 3, instead of in March. Modified some of the 12th Amendment process of choosing a president.
21. **Repeal of prohibition (1933)** Repealed the 18th Amendment. Alcohol was legal again.
22. **Limit on presidential terms (1951)** A president can serve only two terms.
23. **Voting in the District of Columbia (1961)** The District of Columbia may have members of the electoral college to choose the president and vice-president. The number will be equal to its relative size if it were a state.
24. **Abolition of poll taxes (1964)** States may not use poll taxes as a voting requirement in federal elections.
25. **Presidential disability/succession (1967)** Established procedures for how the office of president or vice-president will be filled in the event of death, resignation, removal from office, or disability.
26. **18-year old vote (1971)** National voting age set at 18.
27. **Congressional pay (1992)** Congressional pay raises begin in the session of Congress after the one that voted for the raise.

Important Treaties in American History

Treaty of Paris (1763) ended the French and Indian War between England and France

Treaty of Paris (1783) ended the American Revolution with England

Jay's Treaty (1794) British agreed to leave the forts they occupied on the U.S. frontier

Pinckney's Treaty (1795) Spain allowed Americans to travel freely along the Mississippi River and settled boundary disputes between U.S. and Spain

Treaty of Greenville (1795) ended the Battle of Fallen Timbers; 12 Indian tribes agreed to give up their land that consisted of most of present-day Ohio and Indiana to the U.S. government

Louisiana Purchase (1803) America acquired Louisiana territory from France; doubled the size of the country

Treaty of Ghent (1814) ended the War of 1812 with England

Adams-Onís Treaty (1819) Spain gave Florida to the United States

Oregon Treaty (1846) divided Oregon Country between the United States and Canada

Treaty of Guadelupe Hidalgo (1848) ended the war with Mexico; U.S. acquired the Mexican Cession

Treaty of Paris (1898) ended Spanish-American War; Cuban independence; U.S. acquires Puerto Rico, Guam, Philippines

Platt Amendment (1902) made Cuba a U.S. protectorate

Hay-Bunau-Varilla (1903) Panama became independent; U.S. acquired control over canal zone, can intervene in Panama

Treaty of Versailles (1918) ended World War I; German reparations and war-guilt clause; League of Nations, U.S. does not sign

Potsdam Treaty (1945) ended World War II in Europe; split and disarmed Germany; eliminated Nazis; punished war criminals

GATT (General Agreement on Tariffs and Trade) (1948–1995) lowered barriers to international trade; 1994, created World Trade Organization

NATO (North Atlantic Treaty Organization) (1949) mutual defense pact among U.S., Canada, and ten Western European allies

Korean War settlement (1953) stalemate—Korea remained split with demilitarized zone between North and South

Geneva Accords (1954) temporarily divided Vietnam into communist North and anticommunist South

Nuclear Test Ban Treaty (1963) barred atmospheric testing

SALT I (Strategic Arms Limitation Treaty) (1972) halted growth in the number of two types of nuclear missiles; SALT II (1979) limited number of strategic weapons and nuclear-missile launchers

Vietnam War agreement (1973) ended American involvement; country remained divided with North Vietnamese troops in the South

Camp David Accords (1978) President Carter helped negotiate Middle East peace agreements between Jordan and Egypt and Israel

INF (Intermediate-Range Nuclear Forces) Treaty (1987) eliminated two classes of weapons; allowed inspection of military installations

START I (1991) and START II (1993) continued nuclear arms reduction up to 75 percent

NAFTA (North American Free Trade Agreement) (1993) U.S., Canada, and Mexico drop all trade barriers

Kyoto Accords (1997) international climate treaty; 2001, U.S. does not sign

Important Supreme Court Decisions

***Marbury* v. *Madison* (1803)** Established the principle of judicial review—the Supreme Court could review all laws made by Congress

***Fletcher* v. *Peck* (1810)** Overturned Georgia law that violated an individual's right to enter into a contract

***Dartmouth College* v. *Woodward* (1819)** State of New Hampshire couldn't revoke the college's colonial charter because it was a contract

***Worcester* v. *Georgia* (1832)** Recognized the Cherokee tribe as a political entity; Georgia couldn't regulate them nor invade their land

***Dred Scott* v. *Sandford* (1857)** Ruled that African Americans were not citizens of the U.S.; declared the Missouri Compromise unconstitutional

***McCulloch* v. *Maryland* (1819)** A state could not tax a national bank

***Gibbons* v. *Ogden* (1824)** Federal government (not the state governments) had the power to regulate trade between the states

***U.S.* v. *Cruikshank* (1876)** The national government could not punish someone for violating the civil rights of individuals—only the states had that power

***U.S.* v. *Reese* (1876)** Declared that the 15th Amendment did not automatically protect the right of African Americans to vote (only listed the ways that states were not allowed to prevent them from voting)

***Munn* v. *Illinois* (1877)** Said that states and federal government could regulate railroads because they were businesses that served the public interest

***Plessy* v. *Ferguson* (1896)** Established the principle of "separate but equal," said segregated facilities per se did not violate the 14th Amendment

***Muller* v. *Oregon* (1908)** A state could legally limit working hours for women (Oregon law had established a ten-hour workday)

***Bunting* v. *Oregon* (1917)** A ten-hour workday for men was upheld

***Morgan* v. *Virginia* (1946)** Segregation on interstate buses was unconstitutional

***Sweatt* v. *Painter* (1950)** State law schools had to admit black students, even if separate law schools for blacks existed

***Brown* v. *Board of Education of Topeka* (1954)** Unanimously overturned Plessy v. Ferguson, ruled that segregated schools are inherently unequal; mandated desegregation

***Mapp* v. *Ohio* (1961)** Evidence obtained illegally could not be used in court

***Baker* v. *Carr* (1962)** Electoral district lines that are arbitrarily drawn violate voters' constitutional rights and may be challenged

***Gideon* v. *Wainwright* (1963)** Poor people are entitled to free legal counsel

***Escobedo* v. *Illinois* (1964)** People have a right to have an attorney present during questioning

***Reynolds* v. *Simms* (1964)** "One person, one vote" principle mandated redistricting in all 50 states based on population; shifted balance of power from rural to urban districts

***Miranda* v. *Arizona* (1966)** Police required to inform all criminal suspects of their constitutional rights— "Miranda rights"—before questioning: the right to remain silent, warning that anything suspects say may be used against them, and the right to an attorney before and during questioning

***Swann* v. *Charlotte-Mecklenburg Board of Education* (1971)** Busing may be used to achieve racial balance in schools where segregation had been an official policy and no alternative plan was provided

***Roe* v. *Wade* (1973)** Gave women the right to seek abortion in the first three months of pregnancy, under their right to privacy

***Regents of the University of California* v. *Bakke* (1978)** Allan Bakke, a white student, had to be admitted to UC Medical School, a victim of "reverse discrimination"

***Richmond* v. *J.A. Croson Company* (1989)** City of Richmond's mandating 30 percent of public works funds for minority contractors declared illegal

***Webster* v. *Reproductive Health Care Services* (1989)** States allowed to impose restrictions on abortion

***Rust* v. *Sullivan* (1991)** Doctors working in government-sponsored clinics were prevented from providing women with information about abortion, even if the life of the mother were in danger

Important Laws in American History

Northwest Ordinance (1787) established a government for the Northwest Territory and described rules that a territory would follow in order to become a state

Alien and Sedition Act (1798) restricted rights of immigrants and freedoms of speech and the press

Missouri Compromise (1820) preserved balance in Congress between slave and free states by admitting Missouri as a slave state and Maine as a free state; prohibited slavery north of Missouri

Tariff of Abominations (1828) protected American industry, mostly in the North, from competing with inexpensive British goods; prompted Calhoun's nullification theory

Indian Removal Act (1830) Indians east of the Mississippi River were to be moved to new lands in the West

Kansas-Nebraska Act (1854) repealed Missouri Compromise and allowed Kansas and Nebraska to decide for themselves whether they would allow slavery—used the new idea of popular sovereignty

Fugitive Slave Act (1850) fugitive slaves had to be returned to their owners; they could not testify in court or have a trial by jury; heavy penalties for anyone who helped an escaped slave

Homestead Act (1862) offered 100 acres of land free to anyone who would farm it for five years

Civil Rights Act of 1866 declared everyone born in the U.S. to be a citizen and entitled to equal rights regardless of race

Reconstruction Acts (1867) known as Radical Reconstruction; imposed military control of southern states and said that they had to ratify the 14th Amendment and allow former slaves to vote

Pendleton Act (1883) government service based on merit rather than on patronage

Interstate Commerce Act (1887) established Interstate Commerce Commission, designed to regulate rates charged by railroads

Sherman Antitrust Act (1890) first attempt by federal government to regulate corporations and break up monopolies; hard to enforce; sometimes used to limit labor union activity

Federal Reserve Act (1913) established a partnership of government and private banking interests to insure a stable banking system and currency

Clayton Antitrust Act (1914) clearly defined limits on rights of corporations; strengthened Sherman Antitrust Act

Emergency Quota Act (1921, amended 1924) limited numbers of immigrants, discriminated against eastern and southern Europeans; outlawed Japanese immigration

Glass-Steagall Banking Act (1933) created the Federal Deposit Insurance Corporation (FDIC)

Social Security Act (1935) social welfare program; retirement and unemployment insurance

National Labor Relations Act (Wagner Act) (1935) established National Labor Relations Board; defined unfair labor practices

Fair Labor Standards Act (1938) standardized minimum wage and maximum workweek; outlawed factory work for children under 16 years old

GI Bill of Rights (1944) education benefits, unemployment insurance, low-interest loans

Labor Management Relations Act (Taft-Hartley Act) (1947) limited labor union rights and emphasized workers' right to *not* join a union or participate in union activities

Civil Rights Act of 1957 first since Reconstruction, empowered federal government to enforce school desegregation and voting rights

Civil Rights Act of 1964 prohibited discrimination based on race, religion, national origin, or gender; equal access to public facilities

Voting Rights Act of 1965 ended literacy tests, allowed federal officials to register voters

Immigration Act (1965) eliminated quotas established in 1924; opened Asian immigration

Civil Rights Act of 1968 prevented discrimination in housing; stronger antilynching laws

Environmental Protection Agency (1970) oversees all aspects of pollution control, e.g. enforcement of clean air and water standards

Equal Rights Amendment (1972) intended to strengthen equality for women; three states short of ratification

Indian Education Act (1972) and Indian Self-Determination and Education Assistance Act (1975) greater power given to tribes for self-government and education

War Powers Act (1973) limits presidential autonomy in committing U.S. troops abroad

Welfare reform legislation (1996) limited welfare benefits and required most recipients to get jobs

Telecommunications Act (1996) intended to increase competition by allowing communications companies to be in multiple businesses and to own multiple TV and radio stations

Important Works of Literature, Art, and Culture

John Singleton Copley portraits, 1750s–1780s, included Revere, Hancock, and many other patriots
Phillis Wheatley poems, 1773, by Boston slave published in England
Thomas Paine *Common Sense,* 1776, pamphlet promoting independence
John Trumbull *The Declaration of Independence,* 1794, this and other paintings dramatize Revolutionary War
Washington Irving *The Sketch Book,* 1819, American short stories popular around world
Ralph Waldo Emerson essays, 1836–1841, transcendentalism
Henry Wadsworth Longfellow narrative poems, 1847–63, helped establish national historical myths
Nathaniel Hawthorne *The Scarlet Letter,* 1850, novel, Puritan morality
Herman Melville *Moby Dick,* 1851, novel, white whale, metaphor of good and evil
Harriet Beecher Stowe *Uncle Tom's Cabin,* 1852, influential novel on the evils of slavery
Henry David Thoreau "Essay on Civil Disobedience," 1849; *Walden,* 1854, a year living in nature
Walt Whitman *Leaves of Grass,* 1855, established new American poetic style with unrhymed verse
Winslow Homer paintings, 1860s–1890s, help shift American art toward realism
Matthew Brady photos, 1861–65, battlefield photos bring home brutal reality of war
Mark Twain *The Adventures of Huckleberry Finn,* 1884, novel of life on the Mississippi River
Emily Dickinson *Poems,* 1890, recluse with an inventive style
Theodore Dreiser *Sister Carrie,* 1900; *An American Tragedy,* 1925; novels reflect American naturalism
Upton Sinclair *The Jungle,* 1906, novel exposes conditions of meatpacking industry; inspires government regulation
Eugene O'Neill plays, performed 1916–57, changed American drama to realistic form; often tragic portrayals
Sinclair Lewis *Main Street,* 1920; *Babbit,* 1922; novels satirizing conformity; first American Nobel Prize winner
Georgia O'Keefe paintings, 1920s–60s, famous for illustrating American Southwest in abstract style
T. S. Eliot *The Waste Land,* 1922, epic poem of modernism
Robert Frost *New Hampshire,* 1923, New England poems over career receive four Pulitzer Prizes
F. Scott Fitzgerald *The Great Gatsby,* 1925, novel of the "lost generation," the jazz age
Langston Hughes *The Weary Blues,* 1926, Harlem Renaissance poet
Ernest Hemingway *The Sun Also Rises,* 1926; *A Farewell to Arms,* 1929; *The Old Man and the Sea,* 1952; novelist of "the lost generation," crisp style
William Faulkner *The Sound and the Fury,* 1929, Southern novelist, decline in American values
Aaron Douglas paintings, 1930s, Harlem Renaissance, African Americans in daily life and themes from African art
Jackson Pollock paintings, 1930s–1950s, abstract art influences many
Zora Neale Hurston *Their Eyes Were Watching God,* 1937, Harlem Renaissance novelist and folklorist
John Steinbeck *The Grapes of Wrath,* 1939, novel about the Dust Bowl
Richard Wright *Native Son,* 1940, novel about the pain of being black in America
Walker Evans with James Agee *Let us Now Praise Famous Men,* 1941, Depression-era photos with text
Edward Hopper *Nighthawks,* 1942, painting of diner which displays isolation of modern American life
Tennessee Williams *A Streetcar Named Desire,* 1947, sometimes called best play ever written by an American
Norman Mailer *The Naked and the Dead,* 1948, classic novel of war
Arthur Miller *Death of a Salesman,* 1948, play paints struggles of an average American
J. D. Salinger *The Catcher in the Rye,* 1951, novel about adolescence
James Baldwin *Go Tell It on the Mountain,* 1953, novel about racism and black rage
Allen Ginsberg *Howl,* 1956, Beat Generation poet
Jack Kerouac *On the Road,* 1957, autobiographical novel of the Beat movement
Joseph Heller *Catch-22,* 1961, antiwar novel spawns a catch-phrase
Rachel Carson *Silent Spring,* 1962, nonfiction investigation of chemical pollution inspires environmental movement
Malcolm X with Alex Haley *The Autobiography of Malcolm X,* 1965, explores African-American radical politics
Andy Warhol Campbell's Soup Can, 1965, silk-screen painting, symbol of pop art movement
N. Scott Momaday poems and novels, 1968–89, focus on Kiowa heritage and Native American struggles
Kurt Vonnegut *Slaughterhouse Five,* 1969, novel highlights firebombing of Germany in World War II
David Mamet plays and movie scripts, 1972– , explore hard edge of American life for lower-middle class
Saul Bellow *Humboldt's Gift,* 1975, novel portrays modern American experiences in a changing society
Maya Lin Vietnam Veterans Memorial, 1982, single granite wall memorial lists names and honors war dead
Toni Morrison *Beloved, 1988; Jazz,* 1992; African-American Nobel-Prize winning novelist
Tim O'Brien *Going After Cacciato,* 1975, novel of the Vietnam War
Alice Walker *The Color Purple,* 1982, Pulitzer-Prize winning novel about poor black women
Amy Tan *The Joy Luck Club,* 1989, novel about Asian-American immigrant women and their children

Government and Economic Systems

System	Definition	Example
Government Systems		
dictatorship	A single person rules with unlimited power. Dictatorship is also called autocracy and despotism.	Nazi Germany under Hitler, Iraq under Saddam Hussein (1979–2003)
democracy	Citizens hold political power either directly or through representatives. In a direct democracy, citizens directly make political decisions. In a representative democracy, the citizens rule through elected representatives.	direct democracy: some small town governments (town meetings) representative democracy: United States since the 1700s
federalism	Powers are divided among the federal, or national, government and a number of state governments.	United States since 1789
military state	Military leaders rule, supported by the power of the armed forces.	Japan 1930s–1945 (formally a monarchy but militarists controlled government)
monarchy	A ruling family headed by a king or queen holds political power and may or may not share the power with citizen bodies. In an absolute monarchy, the ruling family has all the power. In a limited or constitutional monarchy, the ruler's power is limited by the constitution or laws of the nation.	absolute monarchy: much of Europe and Russia before World War I constitutional monarchy: United Kingdom has formal monarch with very limited powers
parliamentary	Legislative and executive functions are combined in a legislature called a parliament.	United Kingdom since the 1200s
presidential	The chief officer is a president who is elected independently of the legislature.	United States since 1789
republic	Citizens elect representatives to rule on their behalf.	United States since 1789
theocracy	Religious leaders control the government, relying on religious law and consultation with religious scholars. In early theocracies, the ruler was considered divine.	Afghanistan under Taliban 1996–2001
totalitarianism	The government controls every aspect of public and private life and all opposition is suppressed.	Germany under Hitler, Italy under Mussolini, Soviet Union under Joseph Stalin
Economic Systems		
command	The production of goods and services is determined by a central government, which usually owns the means of production. Also called a planned economy.	former Soviet Union
communism	All means of production—land, mines, factories, railroads, and businesses—are owned by the people, private property does not exist, and all goods and services are shared equally.	former Soviet Union
free enterprise	Businesses are privately owned and operate competitively for profit, with minimal government interference. Also called capitalism	United States
market	The production of goods and services is determined by the demand from consumers. Also called a demand economy.	United States
mixed	A combination of command and market economies is designed to provide goods and services so that all people will benefit.	United Kingdom 1945–1979. present-day Israel
socialism	The means of production are owned by the public and operate for the welfare of all.	Current Denmark and Sweden (government owns some industries and operates them for the public good)
traditional	Goods and services are exchanged without the use of money. Also called barter.	Many Native American civilizations before European contact

Geographic Features of U.S. Regions

Climate	Vegetation	Land Forms and Bodies of Water
NORTHEAST		
Warm summer continental Cool summer continental Humid Subtropical	Temperate broadleaf and mixed forest	Great Lakes (Huron, Ontario, Erie) Atlantic coastline Green Mountains Adirondack Mountains Hudson River Connecticut River Ohio River
NORTHCENTRAL (MIDWEST)		
Appalachian Mountains Mississippi River Tennessee River Atlantic coastline Gulf of Mexico	Temperate broadleaf and mixed forest Temperate grasslands, savannas, shrublands Temperate coniferous forest	Great Lakes (Michigan, Superior) Mississippi River Missouri River Great Plains Lake of the Ozarks Black Hills
SOUTHEAST		
Humid subtropical Tropical wet and dry	Temperate coniferous forest Temperate broadleaf and mixed forest Flooded grassland and savanna	Appalachian Mountains Mississippi River Tennessee River Atlantic coastline Gulf of Mexico
NORTHWEST (includes Alaska)		

Semiarid
Desert
Mediterranean
Marine west coast
Subarctic (Alaska)
Highlands
Arid
	Temperate coniferous forest
	Temperate grasslands, savannas,
	  shrublands
	Temperate broadleaf forest (includes
	  rain forest)
	Mediterranean shrub
	Desert and dry shrub
	Tundra (Alaska)
	Northern coniferous forest (Alaska)
		Great Salt Lake
		Cascade Range
		Columbia River
		Rocky Mountains
		Pacific coastline
		Sierra Nevada Mountains
		Alaskan coastline

SOUTHWEST (includes Hawaii)		

Mediterranean
Semiarid
Arid
Tropical Rainforest (Hawaii)
Humid subtropical
Highlands
	Desert and dry shrub
	Mediterranean shrub
	Temperate grasslands, savannas,
	  shrublands
	Temperate coniferous forest
	Tropical moist broadleaf, includes
	  rainforest (Hawaii)
	Tropical grassland and savanna (Hawaii)
		Pacific coastline
		Rio Grande River
		Colorado River
		Sierra Nevada Mountains
		Rocky Mountains
		Mojave Desert
		Grand Canyon
		Painted Desert

Presidents of the United States

President	Years in Office	Birth State	Political Party	Key Events During Term in Office
George Washington (1732–1799)	1789–1797	VA	none	Bill of Rights Whiskey Rebellion cotton gin invented
John Adams (1735–1826)	1797–1801	MA	Federalist	XYZ Affair Alien and Sedition Acts
Thomas Jefferson (1743–1826)	1801–1809	VA	Democratic-Republican	*Marbury* v. *Madison* Louisiana Purchase Embargo of 1807
James Madison (1751–1836)	1809–1817	VA	Democratic-Republican	War of 1812 American System
James Monroe (1758–1831)	1817–1825	VA	Democratic-Republican	industrialization Missouri Compromise Monroe Doctrine
John Quincy Adams (1767–1848)	1825–1829	MA	Democratic-Republican	Erie Canal Tariff of Abominations
Andrew Jackson (1767–1845)	1829–1837	SC	Democrat	Nullification and bank war Jacksonian Democracy Indian Removal Act
Martin Van Buren (1782–1862)	1837–1841	NY	Democrat	Trail of Tears Panic of 1837
William H. Harrison (1773–1841)	1841	VA	Whig	1st President to die in office
John Tyler (1790–1862)	1841–1845	VA	Whig	Irish and German immigrants Oregon Trail
James K. Polk (1795–1849)	1845–1849	NC	Democrat	Texas annexation and Mexican War Gold Rush Seneca Falls Convention
Zachary Taylor (1784–1850)	1849–1850	VA	Whig	Fugitive Slave Act
Millard Filmore (1800–1874)	1850–1853	NY	Whig	Compromise of 1850 *Uncle Tom's Cabin*
Franklin Pierce (1804–1869)	1853–1857	NH	Democrat	Bleeding Kansas Gadsden Purchase
James Buchanan (1791–1868)	1857–1861	PA	Democrat	*Dred Scott* Harpers Ferry raid
Abraham Lincoln (1809–1865)	1861–1865	KY	Republican	Secession and Civil War Emancipation Proclamation first President assassinated
Andrew Johnson (1808–1875)	1865–1869	NC	Democrat	13th and 14th amendments Radical Reconstruction impeachment trial sharecropping in the South
Ulysses S. Grant (1822–1885)	1869–1877	OH	Republican	15th amendment transcontinental railroad Panic of 1873 Battle of Little Big Horn
Rutherford B. Hayes (1822–1893)	1877–1881	OH	Republican	Compromise of 1877 labor unions and strikes
James A. Garfield (1831–1881)	1881	OH	Republican	assassinated
Chester A. Arthur (1829–1886)	1881–1885	VT	Republican	Standard Oil trust created Edison lights up New York City

Presents of the United States *continued*

President	Years in Office	Birth State	Political Party	Key Events During Term in Office
Grover Cleveland (1837–1908)	1885–1889	NJ	Democrat	Dawes Act Samuel Gompers and AFL
Benjamin Harrison (1833–1901)	1889–1893	OH	Republican	Wounded Knee Massacre Sherman Anti-Trust Act Populism and Hull House founded
Grover Cleveland (1837–1908)	1893–1897	NJ	Democrat	*Plessy v. Ferguson* Pullman strike Tammany Hall
William McKinley (1843–1901)	1897–1901	OH	Republican	new immigrants Spanish-American War Open Door policy
Theodore Roosevelt (1858–1919)	1901–1909	NY	Republican	Progressivism Square Deal and Big Stick Diplomacy
William H. Taft (1857–1930)	1909–1913	OHa	Republican	Dollar diplomacy NAACP founded
Woodrow Wilson (1856–1924)	1913–1921	VA	Democrat	WWI and League of Nations 18th and 19th amendments
Warren G. Harding (1865–1923)	1921–1923	OH	Republican	Tea Pot Dome scandal cars and planes alter America
Calvin Coolidge (1872–1933)	1923–1929	VT	Republican	Jazz Age Harlem Renaissance
Herbert C. Hoover (1874–1964)	1929–1933	IA	Republican	Stock Market Crash Depression and Dust Bowl
Franklin D. Roosevelt (1882–1945)	1933–1945	NY	Democrat	1st and 2nd New Deal WWII and Holocaust Japanese Internment
Harry S Truman (1884–1972)	1945–1953	MO	Democrat	A-bomb and Marshall Plan Cold War begins and Korean War United Nations created
Dwight D. Eisenhower (1890–1969)	1953–1961	TX	Republican	McCarthyism; *Brown v. Board of Education* Highway Act and suburbs rock 'n' roll and youth culture
John F. Kennedy (1917–1963)	1961–1963	MA	Democrat	Camelot & March on Washington Cuban Missile Crisis; assassination
Lyndon B. Johnson (1908–1973)	1963–1969	TX	Democrat	Civil and Voting Rights acts M.L. King assassinated escalation in Vietnam anti-war and counter culture Great Society
Richard M. Nixon (1913–1994)	1969–1974	CA	Republican	feminism; environmentalism U.S. pulls out of Vietnam China visit; Watergate; resigns
Gerald R. Ford (1913–)	1974–1977	NE	Republican	pardons Nixon
James E. Carter, Jr. (1924–)	1977–1981	GA	Democrat	stagflation / energy crisis hostages in Iran
Ronald W. Reagan (1911–2004)	1981–1989	IL	Republican	rise of conservatism Cold War ends
George H. W. Bush (1924–)	1989–1993	MA	Republican	Persian Gulf War
William J. Clinton (1946–)	1993–2001	AR	Democrat	NAFTA impeachment
George W. Bush (1946–)	2001–	CT	Republican	war on terrorism; Patriot Act; invasion of Iraq

Key People in American History

Abigail Adams (1744–1818) Wife of President John Adams; "Remember the Ladies"

Samuel Adams (1722–1803) Revolutionary leader—Sons of Liberty; antifederalist

Jane Addams (1860–1935) Cofounder of Hull House; 1931 Nobel Peace Prize

Susan B. Anthony (1820–1906) Women's rights leader—National Woman Suffrage Association

Neil Armstrong (1930–) American astronaut—first person to land on the moon, 1969

Bernard M. Baruch (1870–1965) Head of the War Industries Board during World War I

Alexander Graham Bell (1847–1922) Invented the telephone, 1876

Omar Bradley (1893–1981) U.S. general during World War II—Africa, Sicily, Normandy

John Brown (1800–1859) Extreme abolitionist; led Pottawotamie Massacre, raid on Harper's Ferry

William Jennings Bryan (1860–1925) "Cross of Gold Speech"; opposed evolution at Scopes trial

John C. Calhoun (1782–1850) Vice-President, Senator (S.C.); nullification theory

Stokely Carmichael (1942–) SNCC leader; coined term Black Power, 1966

Andrew Carnegie (1835–1919) Carnegie Steel; "robber baron"; philanthropist

Rachel Carson (1907–1964) Marine biologist; author of Silent Spring, 1962

Fidel Castro (1926–) Communist leader of Cuba; led 1959 revolution

César Chávez (1927–1993) Formed United Farm Workers Organizing Committee, 1962

Shirley Chisholm (1924–) First black woman elected to Congress, 1968

Winston Churchill (1874–1965) Inspirational British leader, World War II; Iron Curtain speech

William Clark (1770–1838) Coleader of expedition to explore the Louisiana Purchase

Christopher Columbus (1451–1506) First European to land in the Americas

Hernándo Cortés (1485–1547) Spanish explorer who conquered Mexico

Clarence Darrow (1857–1938) Defended John Scopes for teaching evolution, 1925

Jefferson Davis (1808–1889) President of the Confederate States of America

Eugene V. Debs (1855–1926) Five-time presidential candidate——Socialist Party of America

Stephen A. Douglas (1813–1861) Illinois Senator; debated Lincoln; popular sovereignty

W. E. B. Du Bois (1868–1963) Founder of the NAACP, 1909; The Souls of Black Folk, 1903

Thomas Edison (1847–1931) Invented incandescent electric light bulb, 1880; phonograph, 1878

"Duke" Ellington (1899–1974) Composer; band leader; pianist of the Harlem Renaissance

Archduke Franz Ferdinand (1863–1914) Serbian leader; his assassination triggered World War I

Geraldine Ferraro (1935–) First woman vice-presidential candidate (Dem.), 1984

Henry Ford (1863–1947) Assembly line, standardized parts; affordable automobiles, 1920s

Benjamin Franklin (1706–1790) Enlightenment thinker; Revolutionary leader; printer

Betty Friedan (1921–) The Feminine Mystique, 1963; National Organization for Women, 1966

Bill Gates (1955–) Founder of Microsoft Corporation; MS-DOS, Windows operating systems

King George III (1738–1820) British monarch during the American Revolution

Newt Gingrich (1943–) Conservative Republican congressman (Ga.); Contract with America, 1994

Samuel Gompers (1850–1924) Formed American Federation of Labor, 1886

Allen Greenspan (1926–) Chairman of the Federal Reserve Board since 1987

Alexander Hamilton (1755–1804) Author of the Federalist Papers; first secretary of the treasury

Adolf Hitler (1889–1945) Dictator who headed Germany's Nazi Party, 1933–1945

Ho Chi Minh (1890–1969) Communist ruler of North Vietnam, 1954–1969

Hiram Johnson (1866–1945) Progressive governor of California, 1911–1917

James Weldon Johnson (1871–1938) Executive secretary of the NAACP in the 1920s

"Mother" Jones (1830–1930) Leader of women's labor movement, 1867–1930

Florence Kelley (1859–1932) Progressive-era reformer; campaigned for child-labor law

Nikita Khruschev (1894–1971) Communist leader of USSR, 1957–1964

Martin Luther King, Jr. (1929–1968) Civil rights leader; 1964 Nobel Peace Prize

Henry Kissinger (1923–) National security adviser to President Nixon

Marquis de Lafayette (1757–1834) French soldier who aided American revolutionaries

Robert La Follette (1855–1925) Progressive-era reform governor of Wisconsin; targeted railroads

Robert E. Lee (1807–1870) Leading Confederate general, Army of Northern Virginia

John Llewellyn Lewis (1880–1969) Leader of United Mine Workers of America, 1919 strike

Meriwether Lewis (1774–1809) Coleader of expedition to explore the Louisiana Purchase

Charles A. Lindbergh (1902–1974) First transatlantic solo flight, 1927

Henry Cabot Lodge, Sr. (1850–1924) Conservative Senator (Mass.); opposed League of Nations

Douglas MacArthur (1880–1964) U.S. general during World War II and the Korean War

Key People in American History *continued*

Alfred Thayer Mahan (1840–1914) The Influence of Sea Power upon History, 1890

Malcom X (1925–1965) American Black Muslim leader, 1952–1964; black separatist

Wilma Mankiller (1945–) First woman elected to head a major Indian tribe (Cherokee), 1987

George Marshall (1880–1959) Secretary of state; Marshall Plan aids Europe after World War II

Thurgood Marshall (1908–1993) NAACP attorney in Brown; first African-American Supreme Court justice, 1967

José Martí (1853–1895) Leader for Cuban independence from Spain

Joseph A. McCarthy (1908–1957) Republican senator from Wisconsin; anti-Communist activist, 1950s

Metacom (1639?–1676) Wampanoag Chief also known as King Philip; warred with Puritans

Samuel F. B. Morse (1791–1872) Invented the telegraph, Morse code, 1837

Lucretia Mott (1793–1880) Abolitionist; women's rights leader—Seneca Falls Convention

Benito Mussolini (1883–1945) Italian Fascist dictator, 1922–1943

Thomas Nast (1840–1902) Political cartoonist against Boss Tweed/Tammany Hall, 1869–1871

Chester Nimitz (1885–1966) Victorious U.S. admiral at battle of Midway, June 1942

Sandra Day O'Connor (1930–) First woman Supreme Court justice, 1981

Thomas Paine (1737–1809) Common Sense (1776); influenced American and French Revolutions

Rosa Parks (1913–) Refusal to move to rear of bus leads to Montgomery, Ala., bus boycott, 1955

George Patton (1885–1945) U.S. general, World War II— Africa, Normandy, Battle of Bulge

H. Ross Perot (1930–) Texas billionaire, 3rd-party presidential candidate, 1992, 1996

John J. Pershing (1860–1948) Military leader Indian Wars to World War I

Powhatan (c. 1547–1618?) Chief whose tribe befriended, warred with Jamestown settlers

Hiram Revels (1827–1901) First African American in U.S. Senate, during Reconstruction

Eddie Rickenbacker (1890–1973) American fighter-pilot hero of World War I

John D. Rockefeller (1839–1937) Standard Oil Company; "robber baron"; philanthropist

Eleanor Roosevelt (1884–1962) Wife of President Franklin D.; advocate for social causes

Sacajawea (c. 1786–c. 1812) Shoshone woman, guide for Lewis and Clark expedition

Sacco & Vanzetti—Italian immigrants, anarchists, executed during the Red Scare, 1927

Jonas Salk (1914–1995) Developed an effective polio vaccine in the 1950s

Santa Anna (1795–1876) President of Mexico and military leader in Mexican-American War

H. Norman Schwarzkopf (1934–) American commander in chief—Persian Gulf War

Roger Sherman (1721–1793) Constitutional Convention— proposed Great Compromise

Upton Sinclair (1878–1968) Muckracker; The Jungle, 1906, publicized abuses in meat-packing industry

Sitting Bull (1831–1890) Sioux leader; defeated Custer at Little Bighorn; killed at Wounded Knee

Bessie Smith (1894?–1937) Outstanding female blues singer of the Harlem Renaissance

Joseph Stalin (1879–1953) Communist Russian dictator, 1924–1953

Elizabeth Cady Stanton (1815–1902) Women's rights leader—Seneca Falls Convention

Gloria Steinem (1934–) Founder National Woman's Political Caucus and Ms. magazine, 1970s

Thaddeus Stevens (1792–1868) Radical Republican leader of Congressional Reconstruction

Harriet Beecher Stowe (1811–1896) Wrote Uncle Tom's Cabin, 1852

Hideki Tojo (1884–1948) Japanese dictator, October 1941– August 1945

George Wallace (1919–) Alabama governor; 1968 presidential candidate; opposed to integration

Earl Warren (1891–1974) Liberal chief justice of Supreme Court, 1953–1969

Daniel Webster (1782–1852) Senator from Massachusetts; noted orator; against nullification

Ida B. Wells, (1862–1931) African-American journalist; antilynching crusade, 1890s; NAACP

Key Terms in American History

abolition—the ending of legal slavery

American Indian Movement (AIM)—formed in 1968 to work for Native American rights

Americanization movement—education program designed to help immigrants assimilate to American culture

anarchist—a person who opposes all forms of government

antebellum—belonging to the period before the Civil War

assimilation—minority group's adaptation to the dominant culture

atomic bomb—bombs using a nuclear reaction to create widespread destruction; ended World War II

Berlin airlift—U.S. and Britain dropped supplies into West Berlin, blockaded by Soviets, 1948

Berlin Wall—prevented citizens from moving between East and West Berlin, 1961–1989,

Bessemer process—cheap, efficient way to make steel, developed c. 1850

big stick diplomacy—U.S. foreign policy of Pres. Theodore Roosevelt which used threats of military intervention to exert influence over other countries, especially in protecting U.S. interests in Latin America

black codes—laws, in Southern states after the Civil War, to limit rights of African Americans

blacklist—names of people barred from working in Hollywood because of alleged Communist connections

Black Panthers—militant political organization to combat police brutality and provide services in African-American ghettos, founded 1966

Black Power—slogan revived by Stokely Carmichael in the 1960s to encourage black pride and leadership

Bleeding Kansas—description of the antebellum Kansas Territory, due to conflict over slavery

bootlegger—smuggler of illegal alcoholic beverages during Prohibition

boycott—refusal to have economic relations with a person or group

buying on margin—purchasing stocks or bonds on credit

capitalism—economic system in which private individuals and corporations control the means of production and earn profit on them

cash crop—one grown for sale rather than personal use

Cold War—period of tension between U.S. and USSR, 1945–1989

colonization—establishment of outlying settlements by a parent country

Columbian Exchange—movement of plants, animals, and disease between the Americas and Europe after Columbus's voyage

communism—political and economic philosophy of one-party government and state ownership of property

concentration camp—prison camp operated by Nazi Germany in which Jews and other minorities were murdered or forced into slave labor

confederation—alliance of states or nations acting together for mutual benefit

consumerism—preoccupation with purchasing material goods

containment—blocking of a nation's attempt to spread its influence, especially attempts to spread communism after World War II

counterculture—American youth in the 1960s opposed to mainstream culture; based on peace, love, individual freedom

D-Day—Allied invasion of mainland Europe June 6, 1944

debt peonage—workers bound in servitude until debts are paid

de facto segregation—racial separation based on custom rather than law

deficit spending—government spending that exceeds revenue

de jure segregation—racial separation based on law

demographic—having to do with population

depression—very severe and prolonged contraction of economic activity

dollar diplomacy—U.S. foreign policy of using the nation's economic power to exert influence over other countries; use first associated with Pres. Taft

domino theory—belief that if one country falls to communism its neighbors will

double standard—granting greater sexual freedom to men than to women

dove—opponent of U.S. participation in Vietnam War

draft—legally required military service

Dust Bowl—areas of Colorado, New Mexico, Kansas, Oklahoma, and Texas hard-hit by drought and dust storms, 1930s

electoral college—group selected by states to elect president and vice-president; number of electors equals Congressional representation of each state

emancipation—freeing of slaves

Enlightenment—18th-century intellectual movement that emphasized the use of reason and the scientific method as means of obtaining knowledge

environmentalist—a person who works to protect the environment

executive branch—administers and enforces laws

fascism—political philosophy that advocates centralized dictatorial nationalistic government

Federal Deposit Insurance Corporation—created in 1933 to insure bank deposits against loss

Federalist—supporter of the Constitution and strong national government

free enterprise—economic system based on private property, free markets, and individuals making most economic decisions

fundamentalism—Protestant religious movement based on belief in literal truth of the Bible

genocide—deliberate and systematic extermination of a particular ethnic, national, or religious group

Key Terms in American History *continued*

Gentlemen's Agreement—Japanese government agreed to limit emigration to the U.S., 1907–1908

GI Bill of Rights—1944 law that gave financial and education benefits to World War II veterans

gold standard—monetary system in which a country's currency is valued at a fixed sum of gold

grandfather clause—exempted Southern whites from the strict requirements applied to African-American voters

Grange—organization of farmers to combat power of railroads, late 19th century

Great Awakening—revival of religious feeling in the American colonies during the 1730s and 1750s

Great Depression—period lasting from 1929–1940 in which the U.S. economy was in severe decline and millions of Americans were unemployed

Great Migration—movement of African Americans to northern cities, early 20th century

Great Plains—grasslands extending through west-central U.S.

Great Society—President Johnson's program to end poverty and racial injustice, 1964–1968

gross domestic product (GDP)—market value of all goods and services produced in a country in a certain time period

Harlem Renaissance—flowering of African-American artistic creativity in the 1920s, centered in Harlem, New York City

hawk—supporter of U.S. participation in the Vietnam War

Holocaust—systematic murder of 11 million Jews and other people by the Nazis before and during World War II

HUAC—House Un-American Activities Committee; investigated alleged Communist influence in U.S. after World War II

immigration—movement of foreigners into a country

impeach—accuse a government official of serious offenses

imperialism—policy of extending national influence over other countries by political, economic, or military means

income tax—tax on individuals' earnings

Indian Removal Act—1830 law requiring Native Americans east of the Mississippi River to move to the West

Industrial Revolution—the change in society that occurred through replacing hand tools with machines and developing large-scale industry, late 19th–early 20th century

inflation—increase in prices or decline in purchasing power caused by an increase in the supply of money

initiative—a way for people rather than legislatures to originate laws

installment plan—buying over time with regular, periodic payments

Internet—worldwide computer network that allows almost instant communication of words, pictures, and sounds

internment—confinement or restriction of movement, especially under wartime conditions; used against Japanese Americans during World War II

isolationist—in opposition to political entanglements with other countries

Jim Crow laws—Southern laws that separated whites and blacks

judicial branch—interprets the laws and Constitution

Korean War—war between North (supported by China) and South (supported by U.S. and UN) Korea, 1950–1953

Kristallnacht—Nazi troops attacked Jewish homes, businesses, and synagogues in Germany November 9, 1938

Ku Klux Klan—secret white supremacist organization that terrorized African Americans during Reconstruction

legislative branch—makes laws

Linotype machine—keyboard-operated typesetting device

literacy test—reading test formerly used in the South to keep African Americans from voting

Loyalist—a colonist who supported the British government during the American Revolution

Manhattan Project—secret U.S. program to develop the atomic bomb during World War II

manifest destiny—19th-century belief that U.S. would inevitably spread to the Pacific Ocean and into Mexican territory

mass media—means of communication that reach large audiences, such as radio, television, newspapers

McCarthyism—making or threatening to make public accusations of disloyalty without offering evidence, as done by Senator Joseph McCarthy in the 1950s

migration—movement from one place to another within a country

monopoly—complete control of an industry by a single company

moral diplomacy—U.S. foreign policy used by Pres. Wilson to withhold support for any Latin American country which was oppressive, undemocratic, or hostile to U.S. interests

NAACP—National Association for the Advancement of Colored People, founded in 1909 to promote racial equality

nationalism—devotion to the interests and culture of one's nation

nativism—favoring the interests of native-born people over those of immigrants

Nazism—Hitler's political philosophy based on nationalism, racism, and military expansionism in 1930s Germany

neutrality—refusal to take sides in conflicts between other nations

New Deal—President Franklin Roosevelt's program to alleviate problems of the Great Depression

New Frontier—President John Kennedy's legislative program

Nisei—U.S. citizen born of immigrant Japanese parents

nuclear freeze movement—U.S. and international movement in 1980s to stop all testing, production, and deployment of nuclear weapons

nullification—a state's refusal to recognize an act of Congress it considers unconstitutional

Open Door Policy—U.S. request that China be open to trade with all countries

Key Terms in American History *continued*

Panama Canal—artificial waterway built to facilitate travel between the Atlantic and Pacific Oceans, opened 1914

Parliament—England's legislative body

Patriot—colonist who supported American independence from Britain

plantation—large farm where a single crop such as cotton is grown by slaves or other workers

poll tax—an annual tax formerly required of voters in some Southern states

progressive movement—early 20th-century reform movement focused on quality of life as well as business and government corruption

prohibition—banning of the manufacture, sale, and possession of alcoholic beverages

Puritan—committed to removing all trace of Roman Catholic ritual from the Church of England

Radical Republican—Reconstruction congressmen who favored full rights for African Americans and decreased power for former slave owners

rationing—limitation on the amount of certain goods people may buy, usually in wartime to insure enough for the military

recall—a way for people to remove public officials from office

Reconstruction—period of rebuilding after the Civil War, former Confederate states readmitted to the Union

Red Scare—fear of communist takeover of America in the 1920s

referendum—a way for a proposed law to be voted on by the people

republic—government in which citizens rule through elected representatives

salutary neglect—English policy of relaxed enforcement of laws in return for colonies' continued loyalty

Scopes trial—1925 trial over the teaching of evolution in Tennessee

Securities and Exchange Commission—created in 1934 to monitor and regulate the stock and bond markets

secession—formal withdrawal of a state from the Union

sectionalism—placing regional interests above national interests

segregation—separation of people based on race

settlement house—community center providing assistance to residents, especially immigrants, of slum neighborhood

sharecropping—landowners give farmers land, seed, and tools in exchange for part of the crops raised

sit-in—civil rights protest demonstration, sitting down in a business and refusing to leave until served

states' rights—belief that rights of individual states take priority over laws of the national government

Student Nonviolent Coordinating Committee—formed in 1960 to give younger blacks a greater role in the civil rights movement

Social Darwinism—application of Charles Darwin's natural philosophy of survival of the fittest to support unlimited business competition

Social Gospel movement—19th-century reform movement based on the belief that Christians have a responsibility to help improve working conditions and alleviate poverty

Social Security Act—1935, provided aid to retirees, unemployed, disabled, and dependent mothers and children

socialism—economic and political system of limited government ownership of business and property and equal distribution of wealth

Southern Christian Leadership Conference—formed in 1957 by Martin Luther King, Jr., and others to achieve racial equality through nonviolence

speakeasy—covert tavern in which alcoholic beverages were sold and drunk illegally during Prohibition

speculation—risky business practices in the hope of making a quick or large profit

standard of living—overall economic situation in which people live

stock market—where stocks and bonds are bought and sold

suburb—a residential community near a city

suffrage—the right to vote

tariff—a fee charged on goods brought into one place from another

temperance movement—organized effort to prevent drinking of alcohol

Trail of Tears—route of forced Cherokee evacuation from Georgia, 1838

trust—consolidation of competing companies into one large corporation

unalienable rights—natural rights which cannot be taken away by any government; Declaration of Independence lists them as "Life, Liberty, and the pursuit of Happiness"

urban flight—migration of people from cities to suburbs

urbanization—growth of cities

urban sprawl—unplanned and uncontrolled spreading of cities into surrounding regions

USS *Maine*—warship that exploded and sank in Havana harbor, February, 1898

Vietcong—South Vietnamese communists who fought against the government of South Vietnam, aided by North Vietnam, 1957–1975

Vietnamization—process of replacing U.S. troops in Vietnam with South Vietnamese troops; Nixon's strategy for ending U.S. involvement

Watergate—scandal involving the Nixon administration's attempt to cover up the 1972 break-in at Democratic National Committee headquarters

Woodstock—free music festival attracting 400,000 young people to upstate New York, 1969

Name _____   Date _____

The Enlightenment and American Democracy

Specific Objective: Describe the Enlightenment and the rise of democratic ideas as the context in which the nation was founded.

Read the summary to answer questions on the next page.

Enlightenment Ideas

- An intellectual movement that spread from Europe to the Americas
- Influenced the thinking of leaders of the American Revolution
- Core beliefs:
    - Truth can be discovered through reason.
    - What is natural is also good and reasonable.
    - People can find happiness in this life.
    - Society and humankind can progress and improve.
    - People's liberty should be protected by the law.

Enlightenment Philosophers

- **John Locke**, an English philosopher, expressed the idea that people are born with "natural" rights. These rights include the right to life, liberty, and property. According to Locke, people have the right to change or overthrow a government that does not protect their "natural" rights.
- **Baron de Montesquieu**, a French writer and philosopher, argued for separation of powers within the government. In his view, each branch of government should serve as a check on the other branches' power.
- **Jean Jacques Rousseau**, another French philosopher, believed in the natural goodness of people and in individual freedom. He argued that government should be formed and guided by the "general will" of the people.
- **Cesare Bonesana Beccaria**, an Italian philosopher, promoted new ideas about the justice system. He argued that people accused of crimes had certain rights, and he advocated abolishing torture. His ideas were based on the belief that governments should seek the greatest good for the greatest number of people.

Effects of the Enlightenment

- Enlightenment ideas encouraged people to use observation to make new discoveries, rely on reason, and question traditional authority.
- The principles of the Enlightenment led many American colonists to challenge the authority of the British monarchy.
- When Thomas Jefferson wrote the Declaration of Independence, he drew on the ideas of John Locke. The Declaration of Independence states that all men have the right to life, liberty, and the pursuit of happiness.
- Many ideas in the Constitution are based on the ideas of Enlightenment thinkers.

Name _____ Date _____

PRACTICE

CALIFORNIA CONTENT
STANDARD 11.1.1

The Enlightenment and American Democracy

Directions: Choose the letter of the *best* answer.

1 Which statement is a core belief of Enlightenment thinkers?

A Only society creates what is good and reasonable.

B Truth can be discovered through faith alone.

C Society and humankind can progress and improve.

D Only rich people can find happiness in this life.

2 Enlightenment ideas encouraged people to

A affirm their loyalty to the Church.

B recognize the natural rights of the government.

C question traditional authority.

D give up their natural rights for the social good.

3 Which philosopher *most* influenced Jefferson's writing in the Declaration of Independence?

A Beccaria

B Locke

C Rousseau

D Montesquieu

4 Montesquieu's ideas led to

A three branches in the federal government.

B the Bill of Rights.

C direct election of the president.

D trial by jury.

5 According to Locke, people have the right to rebel against or abolish the government when it

A relies only on reason.

B does not protect people's "natural" rights.

C is a monarchy.

D does not have separation of powers.

6 The ideas of the Enlightenment encouraged people of the new United States to

A be loyal to the new government.

B form a government based on law and reason.

C rely on traditional forms of government.

D recognize the rights of the British government.

REVIEW

CALIFORNIA CONTENT
STANDARD 11.1.2

The Origins of the American Political System

Specific Objective: Analyze the ideological origins of the American Revolution, including the Founding Fathers' philosophy of unalienable natural rights, the debates on the drafting and ratification of the Constitution, and the addition of the Bill of Rights.

Read the summary and charts to answer questions on the next page.

Ideas Behind the American Revolution

In the Declaration of Independence, Thomas Jefferson drew on the writings of John Locke. Locke was a British philosopher who said that if government became tyrannical people should resist it.

Locke's Ideas	Ideas in the Declaration of Independence
People are born with natural rights of life, liberty and property.	American colonists had unalienable rights that the king could not take away. These rights are life, liberty, and the pursuit of happiness.
Government has power by the consent of the people. People have the right to change or abolish a government that does not protect their natural rights.	People have the right to "alter or abolish" a government that threatens their unalienable rights.

Debates on Drafting the Constitution

At the Constitutional Convention in 1787, delegates from the states debated many issues as they created a new form of government. The chart below summarizes these debates.

Key Issues	Resolution
North versus South Should slaves be counted as population for determining congressional representation?	The Three-Fifths Compromise allowed for three-fifths of a state's slaves to be counted as population.
Division of Powers How should power be divided between the states and the federal government?	The Constitution gives delegated powers, such as control of foreign affairs, to the federal government. The states are given reserved powers, such as supervising education.
Separation of Powers How can the authority of the federal government be limited?	The Constitution created three branches of government—executive, legislative, and judicial. Each branch limits the power of the others in a system of checks and balances.

The Bill of Rights

At least nine states needed to ratify, or approve, the Constitution. Opponents, called Antifederalists, argued that the Constitution lacked protection of individual rights. Supporters, called Federalists, said that the Constitution gave only limited powers to the national government. The Federalists finally promised to add a Bill of Rights to the Constitution so that it would be ratified.

The Bill of Rights is the first ten amendments to the Constitution. It is a summary of citizens' rights and freedoms.

PRACTICE

CALIFORNIA CONTENT
STANDARD 11.1.2

The Origins of the
American Political System

Directions: Choose the letter of the *best* answer.

1 **The Declaration of Independence states that all people have unalienable rights, which are rights**

A   given by the consent of the people.

B   to be free of taxation.

C   that the government cannot take away.

D   that Congress can grant.

2 **An unalienable right listed in the Declaration of Independence is**

A   private property.

B   the right to bear arms.

C   freedom of speech.

D   the pursuit of happiness.

3 **How does the Constitution limit the power of the federal government?**

A   by refusing to have a single executive leader

B   by ensuring that both large and small states are fairly represented

C   by giving the states power to control foreign affairs

D   by checks and balances among the three branches of government

4 **Which statement is a reason the Antifederalists opposed the Constitution?**

A   They wanted the federal government to have more power.

B   They thought the Constitution did not protect individual rights.

C   They wanted large states to have more representatives in Congress.

D   They were against a system of checks and balances.

"A bill of rights is what the people are entitled to against every government on earth . . . and what no just government should refuse."

—Thomas Jefferson to James Madison, December 1787

---

5 **Thomas Jefferson supported the Constitution. What does this quotation show about his attitude toward the Antifederalists?**

A   He thought they were dangerous to the country's future.

B   He thought they were too worried about the need for a bill of rights.

C   He agreed with their call for a bill of rights.

D   He decided to join them in fighting ratification of the Constitution.

6 **What promise caused the Constitution to be ratified?**

A   The Antifederalists promised to accept George Washington as president.

B   The Federalists promised to give states more reserved powers.

C   The Antifederalists promised to add a system of checks and balances.

D   The Federalists promised to add a bill of rights.

Name _____ Date _____

REVIEW

CALIFORNIA CONTENT
STANDARD 11.1.3

The History of the Constitution

Specific Objective: Understand the history of the Constitution after 1787 with emphasis on federal versus state authority and growing democratization.

Read the summary and charts to answer questions on the next page.

States' Rights vs. Federal Authority The Constitution is the supreme law of the land. In matters that concern the nation as a whole, a strong central government composed of three branches takes precedence over any individual state government. However, the Constitution reserves certain powers for the states. Disagreements between states' rights and federal authority led to conflicts such as the Nullification Crisis and the Civil War.

Event	Issue	Outcome
Nullification Crisis In 1832 South Carolina moved to nullify, or declare illegal, tariff laws passed by Congress in 1828 and 1832. South Carolina threatened to secede if the tariffs were enforced.	Vice President John C. Calhoun, from South Carolina, developed a nullification theory. He said that a state had the right to nullify a federal law within its borders and to withdraw from the Union if it were not allowed to nullify a federal law.	President Andrew Jackson saw South Carolina's actions as a direct challenge to the Constitution as the supreme law of the land. He threatened to use federal troops to enforce the law. Congress lowered tariffs, avoiding confrontation.
The Civil War (1861–1865) After the election of Abraham Lincoln in 1860, South Carolina was the first state to secede from Union.	Most Southerners saw the conflict over slavery as a struggle between the states' rights of self-determination and federal control. The Confederacy declared that states' rights took precedence over the Union, the Constitution, and federal laws.	Lincoln said states did not have the right to secede. When Confederate troops fired on Fort Sumter, a Union fort in South Carolina, the Civil War began. The Union victory four years later led to the abolition of slavery and the readmission of the Confederate states to the Union.

Expansion of Democracy The Bill of Rights did not extend to all Americans. The Constitution has been amended to allow more citizens to participate in the government.

Amendment	Date Ratified	Effects
13th	1865	• Abolished slavery throughout the United States
14th	1868	• Gave all citizens equal protection under the law • Gave citizenship to those born or naturalized in the country
15th	1870	• No one may be prevented from voting due to "race, color, or previous condition of servitude" • Resulted in literacy tests, poll taxes, and grandfather clauses to limit voting rights of African Americans
19th	1920	• Gave women the right to vote
24th	1964	• Abolished poll tax
26th	1971	• Gave 18 year-olds the right to vote

Name _____   Date _____

PRACTICE

CALIFORNIA CONTENT
STANDARD 11.1.3

The History of the Constitution

Directions: Choose the letter of the *best* answer.

1 Which laws are the supreme law of the land?

A   state laws

B   executive orders

C   federal laws

D   the Constitution

2 The Nullification Crisis occurred as a result of

A   an unpopular tariff.

B   the expansion of voting rights.

C   the expansion of slavery.

D   an unpopular bank.

3 The nullification theory declared that

A   the federal government had no right to regulate trade.

B   a state had the right to declare a federal law invalid.

C   the Constitution was the highest law of the land.

D   the election of 1832 was improper.

4 The Civil War was fought over a state's right to

A   abolish slavery.

B   pass its own tariffs.

C   regulate voting.

D   secede from the Union.

5 In practice, what effect did the 15th Amendment have on voting rights?

A   It ensured that every eligible American voted.

B   It led to new laws to limit voting by African Americans.

C   It gave the vote to African-American men and women in the North.

D   It did not affect voting rights.

6 The 19th, 24th, and 26th amendments expanded

A   the rights of the states.

B   rights for African Americans.

C   rights for women.

D   voting rights in the United States.

Name _____ Date _____

Effects of the Civil War, Reconstruction, and the Industrial Revolution

Specific Objective: Examine the effects of the Civil War and Reconstruction and of the Industrial Revolution, including demographic shifts and the emergence in the late nineteenth century of the United States as a world power.

Read the chart to answer questions on the next page.

Event	Effects
Civil War and Reconstruction	• The need for war supplies during the Civil War led to rapid growth of industry and cities in the North. • The Civil War destroyed the South's economy. Because the war was fought mostly in the South, its bridges, roads, and farmlands were destroyed. Property values declined, personal and government debts increased, and the population suffered devastating losses. • New labor systems such as the contract system and sharecropping kept many former slaves locked in a cycle of debt and poverty. • Constitutional amendments and other laws abolished slavery and guaranteed basic rights of former slaves. African Americans became educated and took part in state and federal government. • Southern states restricted African-American voting rights through literacy tests and poll taxes. Grandfather clauses allowed many poor illiterate whites to vote but discriminated against African Americans. The Supreme Court ruled that these laws did not refer specifically to race and so did not violate the 15th Amendment. • Jim Crow laws established segregation. In *Plessy* v. *Ferguson* (1896), the Supreme Court said that "separate but equal" facilities did not violate the 14th Amendment. **Demographic Shift** • Both sides lost thousands of young men. • African Americans moved from rural to urban South; in some cities, African Americans became the majority. African Americans also moved to Northern cities and to the West.
Industrial Revolution	• The United States shifted from a mostly rural to an industrial society after the Civil War. • Railroad lines expanded. People, raw materials, farm produce, and finished products could be moved quickly throughout the country. **Demographic Shift** • Mechanization of farming displaced many farm workers, especially African Americans. **U.S. Emergence as a World Power** • In the late 19th century, U.S. industry made more products than American citizens could consume. The United States looked abroad for raw materials for manufacturing and new markets for selling U.S. goods. The need for foreign trade was a factor in the growth of American imperialism.

Name _____ Date _____

Effects of the Civil War, Reconstruction, and the Industrial Revolution

Directions: Choose the letter of the *best* answer.

1 Which statement describes an effect of the Civil War?

  A Southern industry rapidly caught up to industry in the North.

  B Industry in the South began to produce a surplus of goods.

  C Industry in the North grew because of the demands of the war.

  D Industry shifted to the West because of the dangers of the war.

2 As a result of producing too many goods, the United States

  A began to look to foreign trade for new markets.

  B cut back production to match the current needs.

  C encouraged immigrants to consume more goods.

  D encouraged rural people to continue farming.

3 *One* of the effects of the mechanization of farming methods was

  A a decline in property values in the South.

  B an increase in personal debt.

  C the migration of rural Americans to cities.

  D an increase in the immigration of Chinese laborers.

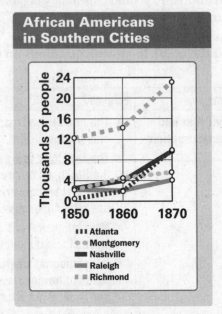

African Americans in Southern Cities

Source: Howard N. Rabinowitz, *Race Relations in the Urban South*, 1865–1890

4 What does the graph show about the African-American population in the South during the 1850s and 1860s?

  A Richmond was the only city with more African Americans after the war.

  B Most Southern cities saw a decrease in the number of African Americans.

  C Many African Americans moved to Southern cities during and after the war.

  D More African Americans lived in Southern cities before the war.

5 How did Southern states *specifically* restrict voting rights for African Americans while helping poor whites to vote?

  A literacy tests

  B grandfather clauses

  C poll taxes

  D Jim Crow laws

Name _____ Date _____

Effects of Industrialization

Specific Objective: Understand the effects of industrialization on living and working conditions, including the portrayal of working conditions and food safety in Upton Sinclair's *The Jungle*.

Read the summary to answer questions on the next page.

Industrialization

- In the late 19th century, industry in the United States experienced a huge expansion driven in part by a growing urban population, which provided cheap labor and a market for new products.

Effects on Living Conditions

- Industrial jobs drew immigrants and rural Americans to cities.
- As cities became overcrowded, problems arose, such as inadequate housing, poor transportation, crime, and lack of clean water and sanitation.
- Multifamily tenements became overcrowded. They were unsanitary and lacked light and ventilation.

Effects on Working Conditions

- Factory employees worked 12 or more hours a day, six days a week, for low wages. Much of the work was repetitive and tedious.
- Many factories were poorly ventilated, and employees often worked with dangerous machinery. Long hours and unsafe conditions led to health problems and accidents.
- Workers in sweatshops, or workshops in tenement buildings, worked long hours without breaks and earned the lowest wages.
- Women earned significantly less than men.
- Child labor was common because all family members had to work to make ends meet. In 1890 there were 1.5 million workers under 15.
- Many children were injured or experienced stunted growth because of the hard work.

Upton Sinclair's *The Jungle* (1906)

- Novel that exposed the poor working conditions of immigrants in the slaughterhouses of Chicago. The public, however, reacted most strongly to the description of the revolting way that meat was processed.
- Portrayed the following conditions in the meatpacking industry:
    - Workers walking and spitting on meat left on the floor
    - Rats running over meat and leaving their droppings
    - Poison bread (to kill rats) and dead rats thrown in with meat to be processed
- Led to a federal investigation of the meatpacking industry and ultimately to the passing of the Meat Inspection Act in 1906.

Name _____   Date _____

PRACTICE

CALIFORNIA CONTENT STANDARD 11.2.1

Effects of Industrialization

Directions: Choose the letter of the *best* answer.

1 The *main* reason for the growth of cities at the end of the 19th century was

  A increasing industrialization.

  B growing cultural diversity.

  C free public education.

  D improvements in farming technology.

2 Which statement *best* describes working conditions in factories at the end of the 19th century?

  A Factory work was difficult but it paid well.

  B Factory work paid low wages because the work was easy.

  C Factories were designed for the benefit of the workers.

  D Factory work was difficult, dangerous, and low paying.

3 Why might a factory owner prefer to hire women rather than men as workers?

  A Factory owners supported women's rights.

  B Women had more skills than men.

  C Women earned lower wages than men.

  D Women were less likely to quit than men.

4 Which statement *best* explains why child labor existed in the 19th century?

  A Children should be seen and not heard.

  B Children did not want to go to school.

  C Work was beneficial to children's health.

  D Families depended on children's income.

5 As a result of child labor, children

  A learned valuable skills and made a good living.

  B grew strong from the exercise of hard work.

  C were often injured or deformed from the hard work.

  D learned to balance their time between school and work.

6 An effect caused by publication of *The Jungle* was

  A the passage of stricter crime laws.

  B the passage of the Meat Inspection Act.

  C improved living conditions in tenements.

  D improved working conditions for children.

Name _____ Date _____

CALIFORNIA CONTENT STANDARD 11.2.2

The Changing Landscape of the 19th Century

Specific Objective: Describe the changing landscape, including the growth of cities linked by industry and trade, and the development of cities divided according to race, ethnicity, and class.

Read the summary to answer questions on the next page.

Changing Landscape

- The expansion of railroads in the late 19th century linked towns that were formerly isolated. New towns sprang up along railroad lines.

- Some cities began to specialize in a particular product, which could be distributed to a large market across the country by railroad.

- Industrialization brought wealth to many Americans, but could also cause severe air and water pollution in cities.

- New inventions met the needs of cities, including the need for space (skyscrapers) and transportation (electric streetcars, suburban railroads).

Growth of Cities

- The early Industrial Revolution in the first half of the 19th century caused new Northern cities to be formed and existing cities to grow larger. Many cities grew near canals, major rivers, and railroads, which provided transportation.

- Between 1870 and 1920 the urban population in the United States grew from 10 to 54 million. Most of the growth took place in the Northeast and the Midwest. In 1890, 40 percent of the U.S. population lived in cities with populations greater than 50,000.

- About 20 million Europeans arrived in the United States between 1870 and 1920. Before 1890, most came from northern and western Europe. After 1890, increasing numbers came from southern and eastern Europe.

- Ethnic groups clustered together to preserve their cultures. Immigrants lived near others who shared their language, religion, and values. They created social clubs and aid societies and put their money together to build churches and synagogues.

- Many immigrants moved into crowded multifamily tenements in the central part of the cities. Improvements in transportation allowed middle- and upper-class families to move to new suburbs.

- Between 1890 and 1910, 200,000 African Americans moved to cities in the North and West to escape racial oppression in the South. They still faced segregation and job discrimination.

Name _____ Date _____

The Changing Landscape of the 19th Century

Directions: Choose the letter of the *best* answer.

Urbanization, 1890

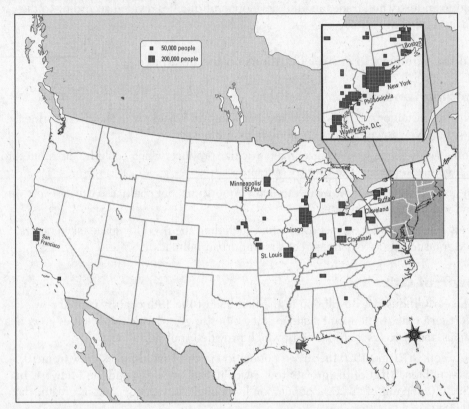

Use the map to answer questions 1 and 2.

1 **The greatest concentration of cities on the map is located in the**

  A Midwest.

  B Northeast.

  C South.

  D West.

2 **Based on the map, which statement about cities in 1890 is *true*?**

  A Most Southern cities had a population of 200,000.

  B San Francisco was the largest western city.

  C Saint Louis was about the same size as Philadelphia.

  D Cincinnati was larger than Chicago.

3 **The growth of suburbs depended on**

  A the invention of skyscrapers.

  B factories being located along rivers.

  C improvements in transportation.

  D the growth of specialized industries.

4 **What is *one* reason cities became divided according to ethnicity?**

  A Transportation between parts of the city was poor.

  B Immigrants clustered in groups to preserve their culture.

  C Immigrants avoided living in multifamily housing in the city.

  D Many rural Americans moved to the cities to find jobs.

REVIEW

CALIFORNIA CONTENT
STANDARD 11.2.3

The Americanization Movement

Specific Objective: Trace the effect of the Americanization movement.

Read the summary to answer questions on the next page.

The Causes of the Americanization Movement

- Between 1890 and 1920, millions of people immigrated to the United States from eastern and southern Europe.

- Many native-born Americans viewed the new immigrants as a threat to the American way of life. They wanted the new immigrants to assimilate, or adopt the language and customs of the dominant culture in American society.

How Immigrants Were Americanized

- The Americanization movement was an effort by the government and private citizens. Its purpose was to teach new immigrants the skills and customs that would allow them to become part of the mainstream culture.

- Immigrants and their children were encouraged to attend public schools and other classes to learn English. They would also learn about American history and government.

- Thousands of adult immigrants attended night school. Some employers, such as Henry Ford, offered daytime programs to their immigrant workers.

- Organizations also offered classes in cooking and social etiquette. These classes were designed to help immigrants learn the customs of the dominant culture, with the expectation that they would abandon their own culture.

The Effects of the Americanization Movement

- Many immigrants, especially children in the public schools, learned English and assimilated quickly.

- Many others resented the idea that they should give up their own culture and language. Some combined American language and customs with those from their native countries. Many chose to live in neighborhoods with other immigrants who shared their language, customs, and religion.

- Labor activists accused Ford of teaching immigrants not to question company management. They believed he was using Americanization programs to weaken the labor movement.

- Catholics were concerned about the Protestant teachings and readings in the public schools. They started their own schools to give their children a Catholic education.

Name _____ Date _____

PRACTICE

The Americanization Movement

Directions: Choose the letter of the *best* answer.

1 The goal of the Americanization movement was to

  A encourage immigrants to live in ethnic neighborhoods.

  B give Catholic children a Catholic education.

  C encourage immigrants to assimilate to American society.

  D strengthen the trade union movement.

2 Henry Ford promoted Americanization by

  A giving money to public schools.

  B offering daytime programs to his employees.

  C establishing night schools for adults.

  D teaching immigrants about American cooking.

3 Which statement *best* reflects the reason native-born Americans encouraged Americanization?

  A They wanted new immigrants to have good economic opportunities.

  B They wanted immigrants to create a more diverse American culture.

  C They welcomed new immigrants to American society.

  D They believed new immigrants were a threat to the culture of America.

4 Which statement reflects a reaction to Americanization programs?

  A Labor activists supported the Americanization programs.

  B Many immigrants resented the pressure to give up their traditional culture.

  C Catholics were happy to send their children to free public schools.

  D Adult immigrants generally became Americanized before their children did.

5 Immigrants preserved their own language, customs, and religion by

  A joining labor unions.

  B attending public schools and night classes.

  C assimilating quickly.

  D living in ethnic neighborhoods.

6 What concern might immigrant parents have had about their children attending public schools?

  A Their children might forget their own culture and language.

  B Their children might not assimilate quickly enough.

  C Their children might refuse to accept American customs.

  D Their children might prefer to work and earn money.

Name _____   Date _____

REVIEW

CALIFORNIA CONTENT
STANDARD 11.2.4

Urban Political Machines

_____

Specific Objective: Analyze the effect of urban political machines and responses to them by immigrants and middle-class reformers.

Read the chart to answer questions on the next page.

Urban Political Machines	Responses by Immigrants	Responses by Middle-Class Reformers
• Emerged in major cities, such as Baltimore, New York, and San Francisco after the Civil War • Organizations that controlled all of the activities of a political party in a city • Offered citizens services, jobs, or favors in exchange for their votes or financial support • Run by city bosses who controlled access to government jobs and business licenses and influenced the courts and other agencies. • Led to election fraud and political corruption	• Got help with their most urgent problems. City bosses offered them jobs, housing, or help with becoming full citizens in exchange for their votes. For this reason, many immigrants supported the political machines. • Some immigrants worked their way up in the political machine organization. Their knowledge of the needs and language of immigrants put them in a good position to secure the immigrants' votes.	• Wanted city government to be more responsive to citizens and more efficient • Distrusted immigrants' power in politics • Galveston, Texas, pioneered the use of a commission of experts to run the city. By 1917, commissions ran 500 cities. • Other cities adopted council-manager forms of government. Citizens elected a city council, which appointed a manager. Usually, the manager was someone trained in public administration. Managers ran nearly 250 cities by 1925. • Some mayors instituted reforms and encouraged citizens to take an active role in managing cities.

Name _____ Date _____

Urban Political Machines

Directions: Choose the letter of the *best* answer.

Source: Copyright © Bettmann/Corbis

1   The cartoon portrays a city boss, covered with a ledger book, taking money from a safe. According to the cartoon, city bosses are

A   careful record keepers.

B   corrupt and deceitful.

C   educated snobs.

D   shrewd business owners.

2   Political machines controlled local elections by

A   exchanging services and favors for votes.

B   launching strong campaigns for their candidates.

C   monitoring voting booths for fairness.

D   sponsoring voter registration drives.

3   Which statement *best* describes why immigrants often supported political machines?

A   Political machines protected immigrants from corrupt governments.

B   Immigrants were particularly concerned about reform in government.

C   Political machines could offer help and services to immigrants.

D   Immigrants were used to political machines in Europe.

4   What role did some immigrants play in running political machines?

A   They kept city bosses honest.

B   They served as a link between their community and the bosses.

C   They controlled city business licenses.

D   Immigrants were unable to play a role in running political machines.

5   Why did the city boss system lead to corruption?

A   City bosses were not elected officials.

B   Growing cities had too many problems.

C   Immigrants had too much influence in cities.

D   One person had too much power.

6   Political machines were organizations that

A   educated voters on both sides of political issues.

B   monitored elections for fairness.

C   controlled a political party's activities in a city.

D   encouraged reform in government hiring.

Name _____ Date _____

CALIFORNIA CONTENT STANDARD 11.2.5   *Trusts and Cartels*

Specific Objective: Examine corporate mergers that produced trusts and cartels and the economic and political policies of industrial leaders.

Read the summary and chart to answer the questions on the next page.

In the late 19th century, the growth of corporate mergers and trusts led to monopolies, in which one company controlled an entire industry.

• Corporations usually accomplished a merger by buying out the stock of another corporation.

• In trust agreements, companies turn over their stock to a group of trustees who run the companies as one large company. The separate companies are entitled to large profits and dividends that the trust earns.

Industrial Leader	Business Practices	Results
Andrew Carnegie Carnegie Steel	• Found ways to make better products more cheaply • Gained control of the raw materials and distribution system for steel through vertical integration—buying out suppliers (coal fields, iron mines) and transportation systems (ore freighters, railroad lines) • Bought out competing steel manufacturers, a practice known as horizontal integration	• Through vertical integration, Carnegie controlled the resources, manufacturing, and distribution of steel. • Carnegie Steel became the largest steel manufacturer in the country.
John D. Rockefeller Standard Oil Company	• Standard Oil entered into trust agreements with competing oil companies. • Rockefeller became wealthy by paying low wages to employees, driving out competition by selling oil for less than what it cost to produce it, and raising oil prices once the competition was gone.	• By 1880s, Standard Oil controlled 90 percent of the oil refining business. • Rockefeller was labeled a robber baron for his tactics

Sherman Antitrust Act

• In response to concerns that corporate mergers were becoming a threat to competition, Congress passed the Sherman Antitrust Act in 1890. This act made it illegal for companies to create trusts that interfered with free trade between states or with other countries.

• The act was difficult to enforce and was ineffective in breaking up big businesses. Business leaders eventually used it against labor union activities, which they claimed interfered with free trade.

Name _____   Date _____

Trusts and Cartels

Directions: Choose the letter of the *best* answer.

1 In a trust agreement, companies

   A buy out the stock of their competitors.

   B buy stock in companies of trusted friends.

   C turn over their stock to a group of trustees.

   D give up their profits to a group of trustees.

2 When a company has complete control over an industry, it has created a

   A dividend.

   B merger.

   C monopoly.

   D trust.

3 When a company buys the suppliers of raw materials and the distributors of its product, the company is

   A practicing vertical integration.

   B creating a trust.

   C practicing horizontal integration.

   D breaking up a monopoly.

4 Which business practice was most helpful to Andrew Carnegie in limiting his competition?

   A vertical integration

   B horizontal integration

   C new manufacturing techniques

   D stock options for employees

5 Why was John D. Rockefeller called a robber baron?

   A He was convicted of stealing from his company.

   B He used ruthless business tactics to enrich himself.

   C He gave much of his wealth to the poor.

   D He stole European art treasures.

6 How did business leaders use the Sherman Antitrust Act?

   A to break up monopolies

   B to discourage free trade

   C to create large corporations

   D to limit labor union activities

Name _____ Date _____

Emergence of the United States as an Industrial Power

Specific Objective: Trace the economic development of the United States and its emergence as a major industrial power, including its gains from trade and advantages of its physical geography.

Read the summary to answer questions on the next page.

Industrialization

- At the end of the Civil War, the United States was still a mostly agricultural nation. Within the next sixty years, the country grew to be the leading industrial power in the world.
- Industry in the United States benefited from several conditions including:
  - a wealth of natural resources
  - government support for business
  - a growing urban population, which provided cheap labor and a market for new products
  - a transportation network of rivers, canals, roads, and especially railroads

Natural Resources

- Abundant deposits of oil, coal, and iron fueled technological growth.
- In 1859, a steam engine was successfully used to drill for oil in Pennsylvania. This practical method of extracting oil led to an oil boom in Kentucky, Ohio, Illinois, Indiana, and Texas. The oil boom led to the rise of petroleum-refining industries in Cleveland and Pittsburgh.
- Coal production grew from 33 million tons in 1870 to more than 240 million tons in 1900.
- The Bessemer steel process was developed around 1850. This process extracts carbon and other impurities from iron ore to make steel, a lighter, more rust-resistant metal than iron.
- The steel industry provided the material for thousands of miles of railroad track. Steel also allowed new forms of construction such as skyscrapers and the Brooklyn Bridge.

Railroads

- In 1869, the first transcontinental railroad was completed. Government land grants and loans supported the completion of the railroad network.
- Railroads provided rapid transportation of people, raw materials, farm produce, and finished products. New towns sprang up and markets grew along railroad lines.
- Railroads had a great demand for iron, coal, steel, lumber, and glass, which fueled the growth of these industries.

Trade

- In the late 19th century, advances in technology led to overproduction in the United States. Farms and industry produced more products than American citizens could consume.
- The United States looked to foreign trade for raw materials for manufacturing and new markets for selling U.S. agricultural products and manufactured goods.

Name _____   Date _____

Emergence of the United States as an Industrial Power

Directions: Choose the letter of the *best* answer.

1 **Which statement about U.S. economic growth is *true*?**

  A After the Civil War, the nation shifted to an industrial economy.

  B The federal government did not support the growth of industry.

  C After the Civil War, the nation's economy recovered slowly.

  D A growing urban market slowed the growth of the economy.

2 **How did growth in urban communities affect U.S. industry?**

  A Urban communities were rich in natural resources.

  B People in cities could not afford products made in factories.

  C Urban populations provided cheap labor and new markets.

  D There was no connection between urbanization and industry.

3 **How did railroads support industrialization?**

  A Railroads invented the Bessemer steel process.

  B Railroads were mostly dependent on oil for fuel.

  C Railroads were big customers of the steel industry.

  D Railroads had a limited effect on other industries.

4 **Which statement is an example of U.S. government support for business?**

  A The government passed laws to limit trusts.

  B The government controlled the oil-refining industry.

  C The government gave land grants to railroads.

  D The government prevented companies from selling abroad.

5 **How did the steel industry affect the construction industry?**

  A The properties of steel allowed new forms of construction.

  B There was not enough steel to meet the needs of construction companies.

  C Construction workers did not know how to build with steel.

  D Steel was too light to be used for buildings.

6 **How did the expansion of foreign trade affect U.S. industry?**

  A U.S. industries could not keep up with American consumer demand.

  B American consumers preferred foreign goods to American-made products.

  C U.S. industries needed foreign trade for raw materials and new markets.

  D U.S. industries preferred to sell all their products within the American market.

Name _____ Date _____

**CALIFORNIA CONTENT
STANDARD 11.2.7**

Social Darwinism
and Social Gospel

Specific Objective: Analyze the similarities and differences between the ideologies of Social Darwinism and Social Gospel.

Read the diagram to answer the questions on the next page.

Social Darwinism

- Based on Charles Darwin's theory of natural evolution
- Wealth, social status, and property indicated a person's fitness
- Poor people were seen as lazy, inferior, and less fit to survive
- Appealed to the Protestant work ethic—anyone could prosper with hard work, intelligence, and perseverance
- Supported the idea of laissez-faire policies—government should not regulate the marketplace or attempt social reform
- Used by Andrew Carnegie and other industrialists to support their business practices

Both

- Addressed the urban and industrial society of the 19th century
- Explained the situation of the poor
- Had some connection to Protestant ethics or religion
- Opposed by fundamentalists, such as Dwight Moody and Billy Sunday, who preached the literal interpretation of the Bible and individual salvation

Social Gospel

- A moral reform movement promoted by Protestant clergy such as Walter Rauschenbusch and Washington Gladden
- Addressed excesses of industrialization and urbanization
- Christians were responsible for helping workers and the poor
- Preached salvation through work for social justice
- Influenced progressive reformers such as Jane Addams and Theodore Roosevelt

Name _____   Date _____

Social Darwinism and Social Gospel

Directions: Choose the letter of the *best* answer.

1 Which statement might be made by a supporter of Social Darwinism?

A Government should help the poor overcome their circumstances.

B People who acquire wealth and social status should work for social justice.

C Government should intervene to ensure a fair and competitive marketplace.

D Government should not interfere with the success or failure of businesses.

2 What arguments might be made *against* Social Darwinism?

A The poor are responsible for their own situation in life.

B Natural law determines which businesses succeed or fail.

C Biological evolution and social evolution are different.

D People become wealthy and influential through hard work.

3 Why might Andrew Carnegie support the principles of Social Darwinism?

A He succeeded by eliminating most of his competitors.

B He was born into a wealthy and privileged family.

C He supported social justice for the poor.

D He favored government regulation of mergers and trusts.

4 Which statement about the Social Gospel movement is *true*?

A It was based on the theory of evolution.

B It preached salvation through service to the poor.

C It preached salvation through acquiring influence and wealth.

D It suggested that natural law determines who is poor.

5 What was *one* effect of the Social Gospel movement?

A It influenced industrial leaders

B It eliminated poverty.

C It influenced other progressive reformers.

D It led to laissez-faire policies.

6 Which statement describes a link between Social Darwinism and the Social Gospel movement?

A Social Darwinism was a response to the message of the Social Gospel movement.

B Both tried to address the social conditions of an industrial society.

C Both said that the poor are responsible for their living and working conditions.

D Both supported laissez-faire policies in the marketplace and society.

Name _____ Date _____

The Populist Movement

Specific Objective: Examine the effect of the political programs and activities of Populists.

Read the charts to answer the questions on the next page.

Forming the Populist Party
• The Populist, or People's, Party was formed in 1892 in Nebraska, building on the work of the Grange and Farmers' Alliances. It was dedicated to easing farmers' and workers' debt and increasing their power in government. • Proposed economic reforms: an increase in the money supply, graduated income tax, and federal loans. Political reforms: direct election of U.S. senators by popular vote, single terms for president and vice president, and the secret ballot. Populists also wanted an eight-hour workday and restrictions on immigration. • In the elections of 1892, Populists received 10 percent of the vote for president. They elected five senators, three governors, and about 1,500 state legislators. • Populist ideas later became the platform of the Democratic Party.

The Panic of 1893
• Farmers, banks, and railroads all had too much debt. In 1893, over 15,000 businesses, including many railroads, and 500 banks went out of business. • By 1894, 20 percent of workers were unemployed and many farm families went hungry.

Silver or Gold
• The biggest economic issue at the time was the amount of money in circulation. • "Gold bugs," including many bankers and businessmen favored backing paper money with gold, which would keep the money supply low and its value high. • "Silverites" wanted paper money backed by both gold and silver. This would increase the money supply and make it easier for workers and farmers to repay their loans. • William Jennings Bryan ran for president in 1896 as a Democrat. He opposed the gold standard and was supported by Populists.

The Legacy of Populism
• Bryan lost the election in 1896 and also in 1900 and 1908. The Populist Party lost its strength and soon disappeared. • Populists had shown that poor and disadvantaged people could organize themselves to have power in the government. • Many populist reforms were adopted in the 20th century.

Name _____   Date _____

PRACTICE

CALIFORNIA CONTENT
STANDARD 11.2.8

The Populist Movement

Directions: Choose the letter of the *best* answer.

**1   The Populist Party built on the work
of groups such as the**

   A   Freedmen's Bureau.

   B   Grange and Farmers' Alliances.

   C   Women's Christian Temperance
Union.

   D   YMCA and Salvation Army.

**2   The Populist Party was dedicated to
easing the debt and increasing the
power of**

   A   bankers and businessmen.

   B   farmers and workers.

   C   African Americans.

   D   women and children.

**3   Which of the following *best* describes
the legacy of the Populist Party?**

   A   It showed that the poor and
disadvantaged could organize and
gain power in government.

   B   It showed that politicians understand
the economy better than most people
do.

   C   After it lost power, many people gave
up hope of influencing politics and
government.

   D   It showed that the country was still
divided between the North and South.

4   The Panic of 1893 involved

   A   international relations between
the United States and European
countries.

   B   U.S. banks, railroads, and other
businesses collapsing.

   C   economic problems associated with
switching to a silver standard.

   D   the rise of labor unions and socialist
ideas.

**5   In a speech in 1896, William Jennings
Bryan said, "You shall not crucify
mankind upon a cross of gold." He
was speaking in favor of**

   A   expanding the money supply by
printing more paper money.

   B   backing paper money with both gold
and silver.

   C   eliminating paper money and
switching to gold and silver coins.

   D   bankers and businessmen who
wanted the gold standard.

**6   Populists hoped to stop election
fraud through**

   A   an increase in the money supply.

   B   immigration restrictions.

   C   a graduated income tax.

   D   the use of the secret ballot.

Name _____ Date _____

REVIEW

CALIFORNIA CONTENT
STANDARD 11.2.9

Progressivism

Specific Objective: Understand the effect of political programs and activities of the Progressives.

Read the charts to answer the questions on the next page.

Four Basic Goals of Progressivism
Reformers did not always agree, but the Progressive movement had four basic goals: • Protect social welfare by changing some of the harsh conditions of industrialization • Promote moral improvement through religious work and prohibiting alcoholic drinks • Create economic reform by limiting the power of large corporations • Increase efficiency in industry and government by using scientific principles

Reforms at Local, State, and National Levels
• Local government—Mayors in many cities were elected who reduced corruption and helped people take a more active role in their own government. • State government—Governors in many states worked to limit the power of railroads and other large corporations. Citizens won reforms such as initiative, referendum, and recall, and the election of U.S. Senators by popular vote rather than by state legislatures. Hiram Johnson was elected governor of California in 1910 and regulated railroads. He allowed people to vote directly on some laws, established labor laws to protect workers, and promoted women's suffrage. • National government—President Theodore Roosevelt tried to strengthen federal regulation of trusts. He got Congress to pass new laws regulating railroads. New laws also required inspection and regulation of food and drugs and established environmental protection and conservation through national parks.

Progressive Party—"The Bull Moose Party"
• When Taft didn't accomplish as much as some Progressives wanted, Theodore Roosevelt helped form the Progressive Party in 1912. It was called "The Bull Moose Party" because Roosevelt said he was as strong and fit as a "bull moose." • Roosevelt beat the Republican Taft, but Democrat Woodrow Wilson won more votes than either. Wilson adopted many Progressive reforms. The party died out in 1917.

Progressivism and World War I
• International problems that resulted in World War I became more important to people than reforms in the United States. • Some of the Progressive reforms were accomplished after the war, such as women's suffrage and Prohibition.

Name _____ Date _____

PRACTICE

CALIFORNIA CONTENT
STANDARD 11.2.9

Progressivism

Directions: Choose the letter of the *best* answer.

1 **Progressives wanted to reform government by**

　A　increasing the participation of immigrants in politics.

　B　strengthening the power of state legislatures.

　C　making the relationship between business and government stronger.

　D　making it more efficient and responsive to the people.

2 **The Progressives tried to create economic reform by**

　A　eliminating the income tax.

　B　limiting the power of large corporations.

　C　restricting immigration.

　D　allowing railroads to control their own rates.

3 **Which reform did Hiram Johnson accomplish as governor of California?**

　A　Railroads were regulated.

　B　The Progressive Party was formed.

　C　The interstate highway system was begun.

　D　Migrant farm workers were organized.

4 **What were the results of the election of 1912 for the Progressive Party?**

　A　Theodore Roosevelt won the election.

　B　The election marked the end of the party and its reforms.

　C　Theodore Roosevelt came in last.

　D　The party lost but some of its reforms were later adopted.

5 **What was the *most* important reason the Progressive movement lost power?**

　A　Most of its reforms were enacted and there was little work left to do.

　B　Its leaders became divided over the issue of women's suffrage.

　C　International problems became more important than national reforms.

　D　The economy improved so much that most of the reforms were not needed.

REVIEW

**CALIFORNIA CONTENT
STANDARD 11.3.1**

*Religion and
American Society*

Specific Objective: Describe the contributions of various religious groups to
American civic principles and social reform movements.

Read the summary to answer questions on the next page.

Various religious groups have influenced American principles over the years. They have inspired
changes in the way people lived and in the laws of the United States.

Religion and the Founding of America

- Many groups came seeking freedom of religion—Puritans, Quakers, Catholics, Jews.
- Puritan New England established traditions of self-government, and family-centered
  communities. Their belief that God rewarded hard work led to the Protestant work ethic that
  focused on individual responsibility and blame for social conditions.
- Quaker Pennsylvania promoted religious tolerance, equality, and early opposition to slavery.
- The Great Awakening (1730s–1740s) used Christian revivals to encourage people to
  question traditional authority, including that of the British monarchy.

1790s—Civil War

- Second Great Awakening—revivals that led to social reform and growth in church membership
- Individuals should seek salvation and improve themselves and society (linked to ideas of
  Jacksonian democracy and belief in power of common people).
- Slaves in the South interpreted Christian teachings to include a promise of freedom.
- Free African Americans in the North formed their own churches, which provided schools and
  other services.
- Beginning in the 1840s large numbers of Irish and German Catholics immigrants faced
  religious prejudice. They eventually increased America's religious diversity.

Reconstruction (1865–1877)

- Free African Americans in the South formed their own churches.
- African-American ministers were community leaders and churches became centers for support.
- Churches helped open the first public schools and universities for African Americans.

Progressive Movement (1890–1920)

- The Progressive movement included goals of protecting social welfare and promoting moral
  improvement. Many Protestant churches supported work on these goals.
- The Social Gospel movement advocated labor reforms, social justice for the poor, and the
  establishment of settlement houses.
- Protestant groups were supporters of the Prohibition movement in the early 1900s. The
  Women's Christian Temperance Union (WCTU) became the largest women's group in U.S.
  history.

PRACTICE

CALIFORNIA CONTENT
STANDARD 11.3.1

Religion and American Society

Directions: Choose the letter of the *best* answer.

1 The principle of a strong personal work ethic is most closely associated with

A Catholics.

B Jews.

C Puritans.

D Quakers.

2 Which movement led people to question the authority of the British monarch?

A the Great Awakening

B the abolition movement

C Reconstruction

D the Progressive movement

3 How were the ideas of Jacksonian democracy related to the Second Great Awakening?

A People were encouraged to follow the directions of their leaders.

B Individuals were encouraged to take responsibility to improve themselves and society.

C The leaders of the government often spoke at revival meetings.

D The government and religious leaders both supported the abolition movement.

4 How did the religion of many German and Irish immigrants affect the nature of American society?

A They were Catholic and increased religious diversity.

B They were Protestant and strengthened the religious majority.

C They were Jewish and fought for workers' rights.

D They were Quakers and fought for abolition.

5 Which statement *best* describes the role of churches in the lives of African Americans during Reconstruction?

A African Americans joined white churches in large numbers.

B Churches helped African Americans become educated.

C Black codes prevented African Americans from attending church.

D African Americans had no ministers to run their churches.

6 Which *two* goals of the Progressive movement had the strongest support from churches?

A creating economic reform and fostering efficiency

B protecting social welfare and promoting moral improvement

C fostering efficiency and protecting social welfare

D promoting moral improvement and creating economic reform

Name _____ Date _____

REVIEW

CALIFORNIA CONTENT
STANDARD 11.3.2

Religious Revivals in America

Specific Objective: Analyze the great religious revivals and the leaders involved in them, including the Great Awakening, the Second Great Awakening, the Civil War revivals, the Social Gospel movement, the rise of Christian liberal theology in the nineteenth century, the impact of the Second Vatican Council, and the rise of Christian fundamentalism in current times.

Read the chart to answer the questions on the next page.

Religious Revival	Leaders	Key Ideas
First Great Awakening 1730s–1750s	• Jonathan Edwards, Puritan; emotional sermons • George Whitefield, British; traveled in America	• Revival of personal commitment to religion • Challenged traditional authority: established churches, British leaders
Second Great Awakening c. 1790–1835	• Charles Grandison Finney	• People must improve themselves and society • Huge increase in church membership
Civil War Revivals Especially the Great Revival, Fall 1863–Summer 1864	• Abraham Lincoln • Confederate Generals such as Lee, Jackson, and Polk	• Prayer meetings and Bible reading • Affected both armies, in Virginia and Tennessee
Social Gospel Movement 1870–1920	• Washington Gladden, Congregationalist	• Salvation through service to the poor • Worked for labor reform • Inspired the settlement house movement and political reformers
Christian Liberal Theology Mid-19th century	• Horace Bushnell, Congregational minister	• Less emphasis on the importance of conversion • Resisted theory of evolution
Second Vatican Council 1962–1965	• Pope John XXIII • Pope Paul VI	• Renewal of the Roman Catholic Church • Opened Catholics to closer ties with other Christians; reached out to Jews and Muslims • Greater interest in social movements
Christian Fundamentalism 1970s–present	• Jerry Falwell, Moral Majority • Pat Robertson, 700 Club, and Christian Coalition	• Roots in the early 20th century, opposed theory of evolution • Literal interpretation of the Bible • Social conservatives on issues such as abortion, homosexual rights, and school prayer

PRACTICE

CALIFORNIA CONTENT STANDARD 11.3.2

Religious Revivals in America

Directions: Choose the letter of the *best* answer.

1 **A prominent preacher of the First Great Awakening was**

A Jonathan Edwards.

B Charles Grandison Finney.

C Washington Gladden.

D Jerry Falwell.

2 **The Civil War revivals were characterized by**

A soldiers questioning the authority of established churches.

B many soldiers on both sides joining the Catholic Church.

C Union soldiers getting involved in helping the poor in the South.

D prayer meetings and Bible readings by soldiers in both armies.

3 **Which result followed the Second Vatican Council?**

A Catholics emphasized that they belonged to the one true church.

B Catholics and Protestants looked for similarities in their beliefs.

C Catholics started the settlement house movement in major cities.

D Catholics emphasized the importance of the conversion experience.

4 **Both Christian Liberal Theology and Fundamentalist Christians**

A began in Philadelphia.

B opposed the theory of evolution.

C were twentieth-century religious movements.

D emphasized the importance of conversion.

5 **How were the Second Great Awakening and the Social Gospel movement *similar*?**

A Both resulted in large increases in church membership.

B Both were led by social conservatives.

C Both were concerned with improving society.

D Both occurred before the Civil War.

6 **Which group was *most* concerned with a literal interpretation of the Bible?**

A Christian Liberals

B Fundamentalist Christians

C Roman Catholics

D Social Gospel movement

REVIEW

CALIFORNIA CONTENT
STANDARD 11.3.3

Religious Intolerance in America

Specific Objective: Cite incidences of religious intolerance in the United States.

Read the summary to answer questions on the next page.

Intolerance toward Mormons

- Joseph Smith founded the Mormon religion in upstate New York in 1827.
- Mormons had some different beliefs from other Protestants. Their practice of polygamy (having more than one wife) was especially troubling to their neighbors. Protestants often threatened and attacked them.
- Mormons moved from New York to Ohio and then to Illinois to escape persecution.
- Their leader, Joseph Smith was killed in Illinois by an anti-Mormon mob.
- The group then followed Brigham Young and finally settled in Utah.

Intolerance toward Catholics

- Most of the early settlers in the American colonies were Protestants who opposed the Roman Catholic Church.
- For many years, Protestants were afraid that Catholics would try to take over the country and make the Roman Catholic Church the official religion.
- Millions of Catholic immigrants from Ireland and Germany entered the United States between 1830 and 1860.
- People in cities opposed them because of their religion and because they were poor and willing to work for low wages.
- Mobs in cities attacked and harassed Catholic immigrants.
- Catholic immigrants in the late 1800s and early 1900s had a similar experience. Nativists favored Anglo-Saxons born in the United States and attacked Catholics and other immigrants.
- The Prohibition movement was largely a Protestant movement. It especially targeted Catholic immigrants for whom alcohol was a part of their social and business life. Many German, Irish, and Italian immigrants lost their businesses that made or sold alcoholic beverages.

Intolerance toward Jews

- Between 1870 and 1920, millions of Jews migrated to the United States from Eastern Europe. Many were driven from their homes and villages because governments in Russia and other countries supported attacks against them.
- When they arrived in the United States, they were often treated poorly for the same reasons as other immigrants—they were poor and willing to work for low wages and people feared their religion.
- Businesses, colleges, and social clubs often refused to admit Jews.

PRACTICE

CALIFORNIA CONTENT
STANDARD 11.3.3

Religious Intolerance in America

Directions: Choose the letter of the *best* answer.

1 What Mormon practice was *most* opposed by their neighbors?

A child labor

B polygamy

C revival meetings

D slavery

2 Why did the Mormon community move to Utah?

A to take advantage of large amounts of farmland in Utah

B because the climate was better in Utah

C to avoid the persecution they suffered in other states

D because slavery was not permitted in Utah

3 What did Protestant Americans *most* fear about Catholic immigrants?

A that the Catholic Church would take control of the country

B that Catholics would take all the best jobs in the cities

C that Catholics would ban the sale of alcoholic beverages

D that Catholics would establish a private school system

4 What group attacked Catholics and other immigrants in the late 1800s?

A African Americans

B labor unions

C nativists

D political machines

5 New immigrants were attacked because people opposed their religion. They were also attacked because they were

A willing to work for low wages.

B members of labor unions.

C in favor of women's rights.

D not willing to work in factories.

6 In the early 1900s, Jews were not allowed to

A build temples in many cities.

B use public transportation.

C attend certain colleges.

D join labor unions.

Name _____ Date _____

CALIFORNIA CONTENT
STANDARD 11.3.4

*Religious Pluralism
and Immigration*

Specific Objective: Discuss the expanding religious pluralism in the United States
and California that resulted from large-scale immigration in the twentieth century.

Read the summary to answer questions on the next page.

Immigration between 1900 and 2000

- Between 1924 and 1965 immigration was controlled by a quota system that favored
immigrants from Northern and Western Europe and the Western Hemisphere.

- The change in immigration policy in 1965 resulted in a new pattern of
immigration. Most immigrants now come from Asia, Latin America, the Caribbean,
and the Middle East.

- Almost 50 million people immigrated to the United States between 1900 and 2000.
The decade from 1990 to 2000 saw more immigration than in any previous decade.

- Since 1961, more immigrants have come from Mexico than any other country in the
world. The primary religion in Mexico is Roman Catholicism.

- California currently receives more immigrants than any other state. For example,
California received almost twice as many immigrants from 1995 to 2003 as the next
closest state, New York.

- California has large numbers of Mexican and Asian immigrants. About 35 percent of
all Asian Americans live in California.

Members of Different Religions, 1900–2000

- The U.S. Census does not ask people to identify their religion. Therefore, it is
difficult to get exact numbers for members of various religions.

- Roman Catholics began to immigrate in significant numbers in the 1840s. They have
grown from about 14 percent of the U.S. population in 1900 to about 22 percent in
2000.

- In 1900, 2 percent of people were identified as Jews. No other non-Christian religion
made up even 1 percent of the population.

- In 2000, Jews still made up 2 percent of the population. Their numbers have grown
from 1.5 million to 5.6 million.

- Increased immigration from Asia and the Middle East has led to growth in the
number of Buddhists, Hindus, and Muslims. Muslims account for 1.5 percent of the
population, Buddhists .9 percent, and Hindus .4 percent.

- The number of people in California who say they are affiliated with any church is
much lower than the national average. Of those who are affiliated there is a higher
percentage of Catholics and Buddhists than the national average.

- Today, more people in the United States and California are members of
non-Christian religions than ever.

Name _____ Date _____

Religious Pluralism and Immigration

Directions: Choose the letter of the *best* answer.

Religious Adherents in the United States of America, 1900–2000				
	1900	%	mid-2000	%
Christians	73,260,000	96.4	238,893,000	84.3
Affiliated Christians	54,425,000	71.6	195,470,000	69.0
Roman Catholics	10,775,000	14.2	62,970,000	22.2
Protestants	35,000,000	46.1	61,003,000	21.5
Independents	5,850,000	7.7	77,957,000	27.5
Unaffiliated Christians	18,835,000	24.8	43,423,000	15.3
Jews	1,500,000	2.0	5,620,000	2.0
Muslims	10,000	0.0	4,200,000	1.5
Buddhists	30,000	0.0	2,500,000	0.9
Hindus	1,000	0.0	1,050,000	0.4
Nonreligious	1,000,000	1.3	25,853,000	9.1
Atheists	1,000	0.0	1,319,000	0.5
Total population	75,995,000	100.0*	283,230,000	100.0*

Source: Encyclopedia Britannica online
* Percentages do not equal 100 as some small groups have been deleted from the original chart

1 Based on the chart, which statement *best* describes the relationship between immigration and religion in the 20th century?

   A Immigration has not changed the religious diversity of the United States.

   B Christians outnumbered Jews in 1900 by two to one.

   C Immigration has brought members of many different religions to America.

   D Most immigrants to the United States are nonreligious.

2 Which statement *best* describes religious pluralism in the United States and California today?

   A Catholics now outnumber Protestants among Christians.

   B The majority of people are now non-Christians.

   C More people are members of non-Christian religions than ever.

   D People are evenly divided among Christians, Jews, Muslims, and Buddhists.

3 Which group was *most* limited by immigration policy from 1924 to 1965?

   A Canadian Jews

   B Irish Catholics

   C Mexican Protestants

   D Russian Jews

4 Since 1961, the largest number of immigrants to the United States has come from Mexico. This has led to growth in the percentage of

   A Buddhists.

   B Catholics.

   C Jews.

   D Muslims.

5 In recent years, increased immigration from Asia and the Middle East has led to an increase in the numbers of

   A Jews, Muslims, and unaffiliated Christians.

   B Jews, Hindus, and Muslims.

   C Buddhists, Hindus, and Muslims.

   D Buddhists, Hindus, and unaffiliated Christians.

Name _____ Date _____

Freedom of Religion

Specific Objective: Describe the principles of religious liberty found in the Establishment and Free Exercise clauses of the First Amendment, including the debate on the issue of separation of church and state.

Read the summary to answer questions on the next page.

"Congress shall make no law respecting the establishment of religion, or prohibiting the free exercise thereof . . . ."

—First Amendment to the Constitution, ratified 1791

History

- Many colonists had come to America so they could practice their own religion freely. Puritans came to New England to escape the requirements of the Church of England. Huguenots (French Protestants) left France to escape laws and requirements of the Roman Catholic Church.

- The First Amendment was part of the Bill of Rights. The Bill of Rights was added to the Constitution to be sure citizens would be protected from a powerful central government.

- In the words of Thomas Jefferson, the First Amendment builds "a wall of separation" between church and government. Today, we refer to "the separation of church and state."

Establishment

- The Establishment clause means that the government cannot decide on a single religion that everyone is required to follow.

- It has also come to mean that the government cannot support one type of religion over another. For example, the government cannot allow one religion to use public buildings and not allow another religion the same right.

Free Exercise

- The Free Exercise clause means that the government cannot prevent people from worshipping or interfere with the way they choose to worship. For example, the government cannot require religions to worship on one particular day or decide what they can do during a service.

Conflicts Over Interpretations

- People disagree about how to interpret these clauses.

- In some cases, the United States has approved spending money that helps religious schools. Other times, courts have prevented it.

- Public schools may not officially sponsor, promote, or require any prayers by students. However, students may choose to pray on their own.

Name _____ Date _____

Directions: Choose the letter of the *best* answer.

1 Which statement *best* describes the reason the First Amendment was added to the Constitution?

A to protect citizens from government interference in religion

B to allow citizens to establish a government-sponsored church

C to insure that a church would not overthrow the government

D to require people to worship in a religion of their own choice

2 Who is known for using the phrase a "wall of separation" between church and state?

A Benjamin Franklin

B Alexander Hamilton

C Thomas Jefferson

D George Washington

3 Which statement *best* describes the Establishment clause?

A It specifies how churches can build establishments, or buildings.

B It allows the government to select which religions it wants to support.

C It establishes the amount churches must pay in taxes.

D It prohibits the government from establishing a state religion.

4 Which of these would be a violation by the government of the Free Exercise clause?

A requiring that everyone repeat the Pledge of Allegiance during church services

B making one church pay taxes while another does not have to

C supplying money for books in religious schools

D preventing people who believe in certain religions from becoming citizens

5 What sorts of rules has the U.S. government made concerning support for religious schools?

A Sometimes the government has allowed spending to help religious schools; other times it has not.

B The government has spent a lot of money to suppress religious schools.

C The government spends the same amount to support religious schools as it does public schools.

D The government will only spend money on Christian schools.

6 How is the Free Exercise clause interpreted in public schools today?

A Schools may sponsor prayers if the whole school agrees to it.

B Students are not allowed to read religious books in school.

C Schools may not force students to pray, but students may choose to pray.

D Students are not allowed to pray during schools hours.

Name _____ Date _____

The Open Door Policy

Specific Objective: List the purpose and effects of the Open Door Policy.

Read the chart to answer questions on the next page.

Background

- China remained closed to outsiders for many centuries. Trade with other countries was prohibited or strictly limited.
- Throughout the 1800s, China suffered from internal conflicts and wars with other countries. It became known as the "sick man of Asia" because of its weakness.
- China was defeated by Japan in the Sino-Japanese war in 1894.
- Britain, Germany, Russia, and France rushed to establish rights for trade with China.

Purpose of the Open Door Policy

The United States at the time had three strong beliefs about foreign trade:
- The growth of the U.S. economy depended on exports. China was a huge potential market.
- The United States had a right to keep foreign markets open. It would use force if necessary.
- If one area was closed to U.S. products, people, or ideas, the United States itself was threatened. The government believed it was protecting the nation by keeping markets open.

Events

- In 1899, U.S. Secretary of State John Hay established the Open Door policy. This policy declared that other nations must share trading rights with the United States. Trade would proceed through an "open door."
- Other nations decided they had to agree. China was not consulted.
- Europeans dominated China's largest cities. A group that Westerners called "Boxers" (because they used martial arts) attacked foreigners in 1900, killing hundreds of Christian missionaries and others. The Boxers were not part of the Chinese government.
- The United States joined with other trading countries and Japan to defeat the "Boxer Rebellion" with troops in 1900. Thousands of Chinese were killed.
- The United States strengthened the Open Door policy by stating it would "safeguard for the world" open trade with China.

Effects

- The principles of the Open Door policy were used to guide U.S. foreign policy for many years. The United States continued to use persuasion and force to keep markets open.

Name _____   Date _____

The Open Door Policy

Directions: Choose the letter of the *best* answer.

1 The main purpose of the Open Door policy was to

  A help China against efforts by other countries to establish colonies there.

  B keep other countries from trading with China.

  C make sure the United States would have access to China's markets.

  D allow the United States to establish colonies in China.

2 Which statement *best* describes the Boxer Rebellion?

  A The Chinese government sent troops to attack foreigners in Chinese cities.

  B The Boxers were supported by the Japanese and attacked the Chinese government.

  C The Boxers resented foreign influence in Chinese cities and attacked foreigners.

  D The United States supported the Boxers who helped enforce the Open Door Policy.

3 Which country benefited *most* from the Open Door policy?

  A France

  B Great Britain

  C Russia

  D United States

4 How did the Open Door policy affect U.S. policy in Asia in the coming years?

  A It established good relations between China and the United States.

  B It prevented the United States from getting involved outside of China.

  C It set a precedent for continuing U.S. involvement in Asia.

  D It weakened U.S. ability to keep trading markets open.

5 What *best* describes China's role in the Open Door Policy?

  A It allied itself with the Japanese against westerners.

  B It was not consulted about what role it should play.

  C It pledged to provide ready access to its ports.

  D It agreed to allow English translations of its laws.

6 Following the Boxer Rebellion, the United States pledged to

  A pull back on its involvement in China.

  B aggressively safeguard open trade with China.

  C make China a more active participant in international diplomacy.

  D hold China financially responsible for U.S. casualties in the Boxer Rebellion.

REVIEW

CALIFORNIA CONTENT STANDARD 11.4.2

The Spanish-American War

Specific Objective: Describe the Spanish-American War and U.S. expansion in the South Pacific.

Read the chart to answer questions on the next page.

U.S. Imperialism

Despite the Monroe Doctrine of the early 1800s, in the late 1800s, the United States decided to become an imperialist power like European countries. There were three reasons:
- To establish military strength, especially naval power.
- To open new markets. Industrialization produced a surplus of goods. Colonies would provide markets for goods and sources for raw materials.
- To spread its "superior" culture. Many Americans believed the white race and the Christian religion were superior to other cultures.

↓

The Spanish-American War

- The Spanish colony of Cuba revolted between 1868 and 1878 but was not successful.
- American businesses invested heavily in Cuba after slavery was abolished in 1886.
- Cubans revolted again in 1895. Spain fought the rebels and treated them poorly. U.S. newspapers influenced many in the United States to want to enter the war.
- In 1898, the *USS Maine* blew up in the harbor of Havana, killing U.S. sailors. The United States quickly declared war against Spain.
- The United States first destroyed Spain's navy in the Philippines, another Spanish colony.
- The United States invaded Cuba with volunteers and poorly trained troops but quickly defeated Spanish troops there. The Spanish navy was destroyed.
- Fighting lasted only sixteen weeks.

↓

The Treaty of Paris (1898)

- Gave Cuba its freedom
- Sold the Philippines to the United States for $20 million
- Gave the islands of Guam (in the South Pacific) and Puerto Rico to the United States

↓

Cuba	The South Pacific
• United States troops stayed in Cuba. The United States wanted to protect U.S. business investments. It forced the new Cuban government to accept some U.S. control over it.	• Filipinos thought they would become an independent country. They rebelled against the United States and fought for three years. The Philippines remained under U.S. control until 1946.

Name _____   Date _____

PRACTICE

CALIFORNIA CONTENT
STANDARD 11.4.2

The Spanish-American War

Directions: Choose the letter of the *best* answer.

1   **Which statement *best* describes why the United States became an imperialist power?**

A   It wanted to keep its current military power and economic markets, and spread its culture.

B   It wanted to establish greater military power, keep its existing markets, and protect its own culture.

C   It wanted to increase its military power, open new markets for its economy, and spread its culture.

D   It wanted to form new military alliances, open new markets for its economy, and spread its culture.

2   **Which statement *best* describes Cuba before 1898?**

A   It was a Spanish colony that had revolted twice to try to gain freedom.

B   It was an independent country that was threatened and attacked by Spain.

C   It was a Spanish colony that prohibited investments by U.S. businesses.

D   It was a U.S. colony that was threatened and attacked by Spain.

3   **Which statement *best* describes the fighting in the Spanish-American War?**

A   It took the United States over a year to win because its troops were poorly trained.

B   The United States won easily and fighting lasted only a few months.

C   Most of the fighting was in the Philippines and the United States won in about a year.

D   All the fighting was at sea and the United States won easily.

COASTING.
The old horse was too slow for Uncle Sam.

Source: Copyright © Bettmann/Corbis

4   **In this cartoon published in 1898, Uncle Sam rides a bicycle with tires labeled "western hemisphere" and "eastern hemisphere," while a horse whose saddle reads "Monroe Doctrine" waits in the background. The basic message of the cartoon is:**

A   Bicycling is a very American pastime.

B   The Monroe Doctrine has been left behind.

C   The world will benefit from American guidance.

D   America must steer a clear path into the future.

5   **Which was the first battle of the Spanish-American War?**

A   The *USS Maine* attacked Havana.

B   The United States invaded Puerto Rico.

C   The United States attacked Spain in the Philippines.

D   The United States took control of Hawaii.

Name _____ Date _____

CALIFORNIA CONTENT STANDARD 11.4.3

The Panama Canal

Specific Objective: Discuss America's role in the Panama Revolution and the building of the Panama Canal.

Read the chart to answer questions on the next page.

The Need for a Canal

- Goods shipped by sea from the East Coast of the United States to the West in the 1800s traveled more than 13,000 miles and took several weeks. A canal across Central America would cut the miles and time by more than half.
- After the Spanish-American War, it was more important for the navy to move quickly between imperial possessions in the Caribbean and the Pacific Ocean.
- Britain and the United States agreed in 1850 to share the rights to a canal.
- There were two possible routes for a canal—one through Nicaragua and one through Panama, a province of Colombia.

The Panama Revolution

- A French company tried to build a canal through Panama in the late 1800s but gave up. It offered to sell its rights to the land to the United States for $40 million in 1903. The French rights were going to expire in 1904. Colombia had to agree.
- Colombia wanted to wait until French rights expired and then sell rights to the United States for a higher price.
- President Theodore Roosevelt wanted to build the canal and was angered by Colombia's attempt to raise the price.
- An official of the French company worked with Roosevelt to help Panama become an independent country. He organized a revolution there in 1903. Roosevelt sent U.S. ships to back up the rebels.
- A few days after Panama became independent, it signed a treaty giving the United States rights to build the canal. The United States paid $10 million plus annual rent for the use of the land.

Building the Canal

- The canal is one of the greatest engineering feats in the world. Work began in 1904 and was completed in 1914. The United States spent about $380 million to build it.
- Disease and accidents killed more than 5,600 workers. Most workers were blacks from the British West Indies. Some came from other countries.
- Countries in South America were angry about the U.S. role in the Panama Revolution for many years. The United States paid Colombia $25 million in 1921 to make up for the territory Colombia had lost.
- Panama assumed full control of the canal in 2000.

PRACTICE

CALIFORNIA CONTENT STANDARD 11.4.3

The Panama Canal

Directions: Choose the letter of the *best* answer.

1 Why was a canal across Central America important to the U.S. Navy?

A It needed a faster way to travel among U.S. imperial possessions.

B It needed a faster way to reach its European allies.

C It needed to prevent Spain from regaining control in Central America.

D It needed to make money to build new ships.

2 Colombia wanted to wait until 1904 to sell canal rights in Panama to the United States so that it could

A charge a higher price after France's rights expired.

B negotiate with France and the United States at the same time.

C build up defenses in Panama against rebels.

D avoid paying a French company to get the land rights back.

3 What was the U.S. role in the Panama Revolution?

A Roosevelt organized the revolution and got the French to send ships.

B The U.S. Congress authorized Roosevelt to send ships and troops.

C Roosevelt waited until the United States had the rights to build the canal before supporting the revolution.

D A French official organized the revolution, and Roosevelt sent U.S. ships to support it.

4 Which statement *best* describes the workers who built the Panama Canal?

A Most were blacks from the United States.

B Most were immigrants from China.

C Most were blacks from the British West Indies.

D Most were natives from Panama.

5 Which statement about the building of the Panama Canal is *true*?

A Great Britain financed the building of the canal.

B The canal was quickly and easily built.

C Colombia was never paid for the land in Panama.

D Building the canal was dangerous work.

6 How did the building of the Panama Canal affect relations between the United States and Latin America?

A Countries in Latin America refused to use the canal.

B Countries in Latin America were friendlier toward the United States.

C Countries in Latin America were angry at the United States for its role in the Panama Revolution.

D The United States offered to pay all the surrounding countries to help provide security for the canal.

REVIEW

CALIFORNIA CONTENT STANDARD 11.4.4

Presidential Diplomacy

Specific Objective: Explain Theodore Roosevelt's Big Stick Diplomacy, William Taft's Dollar Diplomacy, and Woodrow Wilson's Moral Diplomacy, using relevant speeches.

Read the summary to answer the questions on the next page.

Big Stick Diplomacy

- Theodore Roosevelt said the United States would "Speak softly and carry a big stick." He meant that the United States would use its influence and the threat of war to enforce the Monroe Doctrine or meet other foreign policy needs.

- Roosevelt was afraid that if Latin American countries couldn't repay their loans from European banks, European countries would gain power in Latin America.

- He added the Roosevelt Corollary in 1904 to strengthen the Monroe Doctrine. He said the United States could act as an "international police power" in Latin America. He meant that the United States was willing to use its military power to protect business interests.

- The United States intervened often in Latin America. For example, U.S. banks paid off European loans in Santo Domingo and then controlled the country's finances.

Dollar Diplomacy

- Taft succeeded Roosevelt and used military power to defeat a revolt in Nicaragua.

- Taft used "dollar diplomacy" around the world. Taft preferred "substituting dollars for bullets." He thought the United States should increase investment in other countries to maintain and increase its power. The government backed loans made by U.S. businesses to foreign countries.

- Dollar diplomacy in Latin America increased U.S. control in many Latin American countries. Taft also used troops to enforce control.

Moral Diplomacy

- Woodrow Wilson suggested using "moral diplomacy." The United States would only support Latin American governments that were democratic and supported U.S. interests.

- The United States intervened in Nicaragua and Santo Domingo to continue to protect business interests.

- In Mexico, Wilson refused to recognize a general who had seized power illegally.

- In the end, Wilson sent troops to Mexico after changes in the government and attacks on U.S. citizens and interests. After a constitutional government was established, U.S. troops were withdrawn.

- Moral diplomacy was not effective in creating a government in Mexico that ruled according to the principles favored by the United States.

Name _____ Date _____

Directions: Choose the letter of the *best* answer.

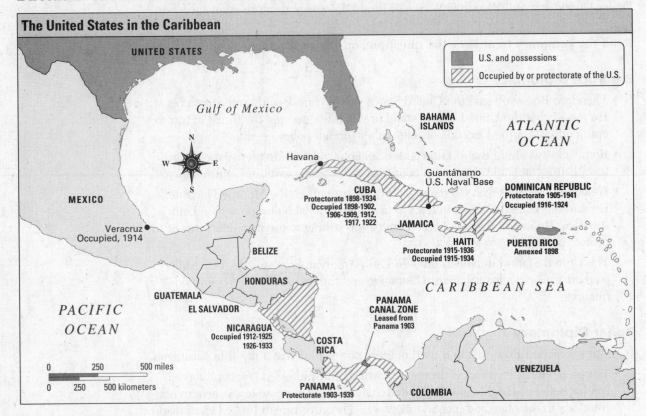

The United States in the Caribbean

UNITED STATES

Gulf of Mexico

BAHAMA ISLANDS

ATLANTIC OCEAN

U.S. and possessions

Occupied by or protectorate of the U.S.

Havana

Guantánamo U.S. Naval Base

DOMINICAN REPUBLIC
Protectorate 1905-1941
Occupied 1916-1924

N W E S

MEXICO

CUBA
Protectorate 1898-1934
Occupied 1898-1902,
1906-1909, 1912,
1917, 1922

JAMAICA

HAITI
Protectorate 1915-1936
Occupied 1915-1934

PUERTO RICO
Annexed 1898

Veracruz
Occupied, 1914

BELIZE

CARIBBEAN SEA

GUATEMALA

HONDURAS

PACIFIC OCEAN

EL SALVADOR

NICARAGUA
Occupied 1912-1925
1926-1933

PANAMA
CANAL ZONE
Leased from
Panama 1903

0   250   500 miles
0   250   500 kilometers

COSTA RICA

VENEZUELA

PANAMA
Protectorate 1903-1939

COLOMBIA

1 How does the map reflect American foreign policy in the Caribbean?

A The United States took a hands-off policy toward the Caribbean.

B The United States wanted European countries to get involved in the Caribbean.

C The United States controlled several countries in the Caribbean.

D The United States was only involved with Caribbean countries as a trading partner.

2 Which theme was common to the diplomatic policies of presidents Roosevelt, Taft, and Wilson?

A They protected U.S. business interests.

B They only supported countries with democratic governments.

C They would not use U.S. troops.

D They refused to back foreign loans.

3 President Wilson's moral diplomacy was tested by conflicts in

A Brazil.

B Colombia.

C Mexico.

D Panama.

Name _____ Date _____

REVIEW

CALIFORNIA CONTENT STANDARD 11.4.5

World War I at Home

Specific Objective: Analyze the political, economic and social ramifications of World War I on the home front.

Read the chart to answer the questions on the next page.

Effects of World War I at Home		
Political	**Economic**	**Social**
• There was much debate before the war about the U.S. role in world affairs. • Some wanted to remain isolated from world troubles; others felt the United States needed to act as a world leader. • The government worked to gain support for war through speeches, pamphlets, posters, etc. • War was backed by most. Strong feelings also prompted attacks on German immigrants and any citizens opposed to the war. • After the war, isolationists gained more power and blocked U.S. entry into the League of Nations. • The United States tried to avoid international involvements until attacked by Japan in 1941.	• The United States tried to maintain trade relations with European countries at war, but attacks on U.S. shipping helped push the country into war. • The government borrowed money by selling bonds. • The government regulated industrial production. • The war effort propelled the U.S. economy to become the strongest industrial power in the world. • Wages rose in industry, but food and housing costs also rose quickly. • Large corporations made huge profits. • Labor unions grew and strikes were common. • Workers were needed in all industries. Women and African Americans were hired.	• African Americans moved from the South to Northern cities in the Great Migration. They escaped some discrimination and worked at industrial jobs that paid well. • Women worked in jobs previously done by men (who were away fighting in the war), including jobs in industry, mining, and construction. They also worked as nurses, teachers, and clerks. • Women's new work helped build support for woman suffrage (passed after the war in 1920). • After the war, many people wanted things to return to "normal" after the many sacrifices and changes of the time.

PRACTICE

CALIFORNIA CONTENT
STANDARD 11.4.5

World War I at Home

Directions: Choose the letter of the *best* answer.

1 Which statement *best* describes
political feeling in the United States
before World War I?

  A Most people had strong feelings but
did not always agree on the U.S. role
in the world.

  B Most people believed that the conflict
in Europe would pass if left alone.

  C Most people wanted the United States
to stay out of world affairs.

  D Most people believed that the United
States should protect its European
allies from attack.

2 Which effect resulted from the
government's program to gain
support for the war?

  A Women used more meat in cooking.

  B Food and housing prices dropped.

  C Labor unions rarely had strikes.

  D German immigrants were attacked.

3 How did World War I affect the
economy of the United States?

  A It hurt the economy because the
government regulated industry.

  B Many men were unemployed after
they returned from the war.

  C It made the United States the
strongest industrial power in the
world.

  D It was a good time for farmers but
had little effect on manufacturing.

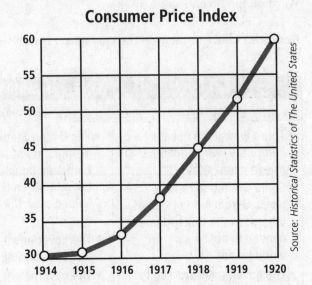

Consumer Price Index

Source: *Historical Statistics of The United States*

4 The Consumer Price Index measures
changes in the prices of goods and
services bought by consumers. Based
on the graph, which statement about
the economy during World War I is
true?

  A Prices remained steady during and
after the war.

  B Prices rose during the war but
dropped when the war was over.

  C Prices rose both during and after
the war.

  D Prices dropped after the United
States entered the war in 1917.

5 Which of the following *best* describes
economic changes during the war?

  A Wages rose and corporate profits
dropped.

  B Wages dropped and corporate profits
dropped.

  C Wages dropped and corporate profits
rose.

  D Wages rose and corporate profits rose.

Name _____ Date _____

REVIEW

CALIFORNIA CONTENT
STANDARD 11.4.6

World Powers After World War II

Specific Objective: Trace the declining role of Great Britain and the expanding role of the United States in world affairs after World War II.

Read the chart to answer the questions on the next page.

Status at End of World War II	
Great Britain	**United States**
• Great damage from war • Economy needed to rebuild • Unable to manage empire that stretched around the world	• Little damage from war • Strongest economy in the world • Able to respond to crises and threats around the world

Role in World Affairs Since World War II	
Great Britain	**United States**
• Unable to continue aid to Turkey and Greece after war in effort to contain Russian influence—asked United States to take over • Colonies sought and won independence, including India and African nations • Economy remained slow in decades after World War II • Allowed United States to take leadership role in world affairs • Strong member of United Nations and NATO • Joined European Union in 1973 to strengthen economic cooperation in Europe	• Quickly took leadership through Truman Doctrine (to help countries resist communism) • Leader of Berlin airlift so that West Berlin could remain noncommunist (Russia blocked off roads to Berlin to prevented supplies from reaching the western sector.) • Engaged in the Cold War to try to prevent USSR and Chinese communist expansion around the world; arms race resulted in nuclear missiles and huge military buildup • Fought in Korea and Vietnam to try to prevent communist control there; Korea remains divided, and Vietnam is a communist country • Deeply involved in Middle East in support of Israel and certain other countries at different times • After fall of communism in USSR and Eastern Europe, promoted trade with new democracies • Currently largest economy and military force in world

Name _____ Date _____

PRACTICE

CALIFORNIA CONTENT
STANDARD 11.4.6

World Powers After World War II

Directions: Choose the letter of the *best* answer.

1 Which statement *best* describes Great Britain after World War II?

   A It had sustained much damage during the war.

   B It was ready to expand its global empire.

   C It was ready to cooperate with Russian communists.

   D Its relationship with the United States was weak.

2 Great Britain asked the United States to take over aid to which European countries?

   A Spain and France

   B Italy and Germany

   C Turkey and Greece

   D Poland and Yugoslavia

3 What was the intent of the Truman Doctrine?

   A to help rebuild European cities

   B to help modernize the economies of Latin America and Africa

   C to help countries resist communist control

   D to force the USSR to honor its agreements after World War II

4 Which of these was a result of the Cold War?

   A greater cooperation between the USSR and the United States

   B the development of nuclear missiles and a huge military buildup

   C a democracy in Cuba that allows trade with the United States

   D a communist government in all of Korea

5 Which country in the Middle East has the United States consistently supported?

   A Egypt

   B Lebanon

   C Iran

   D Israel

6 Which statement *best* describes the current position of the United States in the world?

   A the largest economy and military in the world

   B a strong member of the European Union

   C a leader in the move toward disarmament

   D isolated from involvement in world affairs

Name _____ Date _____

Specific Objective: Discuss the policies of Warren Harding, Calvin Coolidge, and
Herbert Hoover.

Read the charts to answer the questions on the next page.

Conservative Republican Presidents 1920–1932
• People looked for "return to normalcy" after sacrifices and hardships of World War I.
• Economy grew rapidly from 1920–1929.
• Republicans won three elections with conservative views.
• Supported interests of big business through tax cuts for corporations and the wealthy and through high tariffs; believed government should not intervene in the economy
• Believed in limited role in foreign affairs and international efforts to prevent war
• Believed government should not act to protect or assist individuals
• Stock market crash of 1929 and Great Depression that followed eventually forced Hoover to take government action to help the economy.

Policies of Warren Harding	Policies of Calvin Coolidge	Policies of Herbert Hoover
• Elected in 1920 to succeed Wilson	• Took over after Harding's death and then elected in 1924	• Elected in 1928 as a symbol of prosperity
• Appointed friends to government posts; some were corrupt	• First cleaned up corruption scandals	• Wanted business to follow government lead on economy voluntarily
• Repealed wartime taxes on corporate profits and reduced taxes for wealthy	• Continued Roosevelt's Big Stick policy in Latin America	• 1929 stock market crash wiped out economic gains; first believed it a short term crisis that could be solved by private business
• Approved high tariffs to protect U.S. businesses	• Resisted government help to farmers; reduced taxes for wealthy	
• Approved immigration quotas to limit European immigrants	• Supported high tariffs; allowed business mergers	• Tried to help farmers and manufacturers by raising tariffs, but the move hurt the economy
• Agreed to arms limits for United States and Europe	• Corporate profits grew for many, but some industries and farmers suffered	• Later, approved programs to back loans for businesses, banks, and individuals
• Continued Open Door policy toward China to insure access to trade	• Supported treaty to prevent international war	• Resisted calls to help people directly with payments
• Died in office 1923	• Did not run for reelection	• Easily defeated in 1932

PRACTICE

CALIFORNIA CONTENT
STANDARD 11.5.1

Presidents of the 1920s

Directions: Choose the letter of the *best* answer.

1   Which statement *best* describes the
    mood of Americans during the 1920s?

    A   They wanted to continue Progressive
        reforms.

    B   They wanted to expand their
        influence around the world.

    C   They wanted to return to an
        agricultural economy.

    D   They hoped for a return to normal
        life after World War I.

2   Which statement *best* describes the
    views of the presidents from 1920 to
    1932?

    A   They favored lower taxes for workers
        and supported unions.

    B   They favored high tariffs to protect
        U.S. business interests.

    C   They did not believe in international
        efforts to prevent war.

    D   They believed the government should
        directly help individuals.

3   Immigration quotas that limited
    European immigrants were approved
    under President

    A   Coolidge.

    B   Harding.

    C   Hoover.

    D   Wilson.

4   President Coolidge's policy in Latin
    America continued

    A   Harding's Teapot Dome policy.

    B   Wilson's Fourteen Points.

    C   Roosevelt's Big Stick policy.

    D   Taft's Dollar Diplomacy.

5   President Hoover believed that the
    government should

    A   establish guidelines for businesses to
        follow voluntarily.

    B   prevent businesses from taking
        actions that would harm the economy.

    C   reduce tariffs to promote business
        competition.

    D   provide payments to individuals who
        were hurt by the stock market crash.

6   At first, President Hoover thought
    that the situation caused by the
    stock market crash in 1929 was a

    A   good thing for the economy.

    B   good reason to increase taxes on
        businesses.

    C   result of industries not producing
        enough goods.

    D   temporary problem that business
        could solve.

Name _____ Date _____

REVIEW

**CALIFORNIA CONTENT
STANDARD 11.5.2**   *Attacks on Civil Liberties*

Specific Objective: Analyze the international and domestic events, interests, and philosophies that prompted attacks on civil liberties, including the Palmer Raids, Marcus Garvey's "back-to-Africa" movement, the Ku Klux Klan, and immigration quotas. Analyze the responses of organizations such as the American Civil Liberties Union, the National Association for the Advancement of Colored People, and the Anti-Defamation League to those attacks.

Read the summary to answer the questions on the next page.

Civil Rights Under Attack

- **Labor unions**—During World War I, workers rights were suppressed. In the 1920s, steelworkers, police, and others went on strike for better pay and working conditions. Owners blamed strikes on "Reds," or communists, and used force to stop them. Many strikers were killed or injured.

- **Palmer raids**—Attorney General Palmer and others feared there was a conspiracy to overthrow the U.S. government. He ordered raids in which thousands of suspected communists, socialists, and anarchists were arrested. Many opposed the government but hadn't violated any laws. Many were deported without trial.

- **Immigration quotas**—There was a huge surge in immigration right after World War I. Nativist fears of job competition along with racist attitudes led to a quota system. Laws limited immigration from Europe and prohibited it from Japan.

- **Ku Klux Klan**—Originally formed during Reconstruction, the Ku Klux Klan was organized again in the wake of the Red Scare and anti-immigrant feelings. It attacked African Americans, Jews, immigrants, and Catholics.

Fighting for Civil Rights

- **ACLU**—The American Civil Liberties Union was founded in 1920 to defend constitutional rights. It fought against the Palmer raids and supplied lawyers in support of Sacco and Vanzetti. It supported the rights of labor unions and citizens who were critical of the government.

- **NAACP**—The National Association for the Advancement of Colored People was founded in 1910 to protest racial violence. It worked for the passage of anti-lynching laws.

- **Marcus Garvey**—A native of Jamaica, Garvey took a more radical approach than the NAACP, focused on black pride. He believed in a separate society for African Americans and encouraged his thousands of followers to return to Africa.

- **Anti-Defamation League**—This Jewish group began work in 1913 against religious and racial discrimination. Russian Jewish immigrants were often linked with communism and labor unrest. The league worked against the Ku Klux Klan in the 1920s and fought discrimination in employment and housing.

Name _____   Date _____

CALIFORNIA CONTENT
STANDARD 11.5.2

Attacks on Civil Liberties

Directions: Choose the letter of the *best* answer.

1 The reason for the Palmer raids was fear of

A   a communist plot to overthrow the government.

B   African Americans taking jobs from native-born workers.

C   immigrants controlling labor unions.

D   immigrants controlling political machines in cities.

2 During the 1920s, the Ku Klux Klan

A   formed a political party that elected government officials.

B   supported the teaching of evolution in schools.

C   was used by communists to control labor unions.

D   attacked African Americans, Jews, immigrants, and Catholics.

3 Factory owners often blamed strikes on

A   women who had joined the work force during World War I.

B   workers who were "Reds" or communists.

C   newspapers that published stories about working conditions.

D   native-born Americans who disliked immigrants.

4 Marcus Garvey was an African-American leader who

A   organized strikes by African-American workers.

B   was elected leader of the NAACP.

C   encouraged African Americans to return to Africa.

D   argued important civil rights cases in court.

5 The ACLU is a group that was founded to

A   promote better working conditions for women.

B   defend the rights guaranteed in the Constitution.

C   work for social reform through settlement houses.

D   prevent immigration from Japan and Europe.

6 The NAACP was founded

A   shortly after the Civil War to provide better jobs for African Americans.

B   in the 1890s to work for better housing for African Americans.

C   early in the twentieth century to protest racial violence against African Americans.

D   in the 1920s to promote artistic freedom for African Americans.

Name _____ Date _____

Prohibition

Specific Objective: Understand the passage of the Eighteenth Amendment to the
Constitution and the Volstead Act.

Read the sequence diagram to answer the questions on the next page.

Early Prohibition Movement

- Early proposals for prohibition began in the early 1800s but were interrupted by the Civil War.
- Strong push began in the 1870s by Women's Christian Temperance Union; Anti-Saloon League started in 1895 by Progressive women; Protestant churches were a strong source of support.
- In general, rural areas supported prohibition and cities opposed it; urban immigrants did not see drinking as a sin, and saloons served some community needs.
- By 1917, about half of states (most in South and West) prohibited alcohol use.

Prohibition

- Congress passed the Eighteenth Amendment in 1917 and states ratified it in 1919. It prohibited the making, transportation, or sale of alcoholic beverages.
- Volstead Act passed in 1919 to enforce the amendment; Congress never supplied enough money for real enforcement.

Effects of Prohibition

- At first, saloons closed; public drunkenness and overall alcohol consumption decreased.
- Later, many people went to illegal saloons (speakeasies) and bought alcohol from smugglers (bootleggers); many showed a general disrespect for the law.
- Prohibition couldn't be fully enforced because of a lack of money; raids and arrests were selective and seemed like an attack on personal freedoms.
- Criminals organized to supply illegal alcohol and became very powerful; many government officials took bribes from them.
- People began to feel the "experiment" of Prohibition had failed by the mid-1920s.
- During the Great Depression, people argued that Prohibition kept people out of work and put money into hands of criminals rather than governments.

Repeal

- Political groups supported candidates who wanted to repeal Prohibition.
- Congress passed the Twenty-first Amendment, which repealed the Eighteenth, in 1933, and states ratified it the same year.
- State and local governments currently have control of alcohol laws; alcohol consumption has increased considerably since Prohibition ended.

Name _____   Date _____

PRACTICE

CALIFORNIA CONTENT
STANDARD 11.5.3

Prohibition

Directions: Choose the letter of the *best* answer.

1   The Women's Christian Temperance Union and the Anti-Saloon League began a strong movement for prohibition

   A   before the Civil War, in the early 1800s.

   B   after the Civil War, in the late 1800s.

   C   before World War I, in the early 1900s.

   D   after World War I, in the 1920s.

2   The strongest support for Prohibition was generally in

   A   rural areas, especially in the South and West.

   B   rural areas, especially in the Northeast.

   C   urban areas, especially in the South and West.

   D   urban areas, especially in the Northeast.

3   The Volstead Act was passed in 1919 to

   A   regulate the hours of saloons.

   B   enforce the Eighteenth Amendment.

   C   allow state control of liquor sales.

   D   prevent liquor sales on Sundays.

4   During the 1920s, "speakeasies" were popular and "bootleggers" powerful because

   A   people respected and obeyed the laws.

   B   the government supported them.

   C   many people did not agree with Prohibition.

   D   church groups helped them out.

5   During the Great Depression, people argued that Prohibition

   A   forced businesses to import foreign wine.

   B   was a successful program.

   C   had contributed to the stock market crash.

   D   kept people out of work.

6   Prohibition ended with the Twenty-first Amendment in

   A   1929, around the time of the Stock Market Crash.

   B   1933, during the Great Depression.

   C   1940, around the beginning of World War II.

   D   1945, at the end of World War II.

Name _____ Date _____

Changing Roles for Women

Specific Objective: Analyze the passage of the Nineteenth Amendment to the
Constitution and the changing role of women in society.

Read the chart to answer the questions on the next page.

Women's Right to Vote

- Many women working in temperance and abolition movements before Civil War were also interested in suffrage (the right to vote).
- Seneca Falls Convention in 1848 stated grievances and need for equal rights
- Groups organized in 1869 to work for suffrage; Wyoming first state to pass it
- Some women claimed right to vote at time of the Fifteenth Amendment in 1870 that established voting rights for African-American men.
- Two groups came together in 1890 and formed National American Woman Suffrage Association; leaders such as Elizabeth Stanton, Susan Anthony, and Lucy Stone formed a national strategy for suffrage.
- Between 1893 and 1914, 14 states gave women the right to vote.
- Before World War I, protests and public demonstrations increased; many women were arrested and harassed.
- After much work by women during World War I, demands for suffrage grew.
- Congress passed the Nineteenth Amendment in 1919 and states ratified it in 1920.

Women in Society

- Women took larger role in public life throughout 1800s, especially through work in abolition and temperance movements.
- In late 1800s, women helped lead the Progressive movement with work toward social welfare and temperance.
- By 1900, 20 percent of women worked outside the home, mostly because of economic need.
- More women attended women's colleges and gained degrees.
- Women played a huge role during World War I, e.g., they worked at many new types of manufacturing and construction jobs, volunteered at hospitals and clinics, served as war nurses, and sold liberty bonds.
- After World War I and the Nineteenth Amendment, women took a larger role in public life through work and had new attitudes about marriage and family—marriage was not the only accepted goal for young women and it was seen as more of an equal partnership.
- During the 1920s, expectations for young women changed considerably; fashions changed (e.g., "flappers" wore shorter dresses and hair), women smoked and drank in public and danced in new ways; casual dating became common.

Name _____   Date _____

Changing Roles for Women

Directions: Choose the letter of the *best* answer.

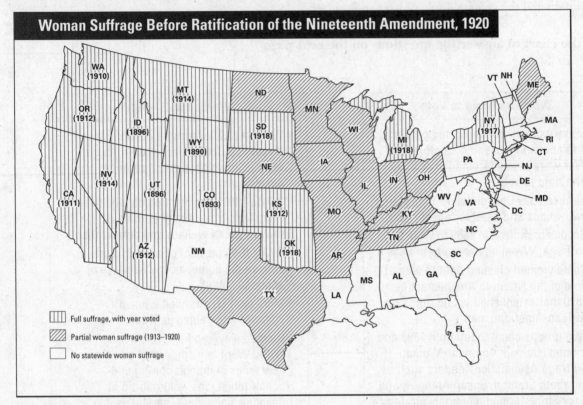

Woman Suffrage Before Ratification of the Nineteenth Amendment, 1920

WA (1910)
OR (1912)
MT (1914)
ND
MN
VT NH ME
ID (1896)
WY (1890)
SD (1918)
WI
NY (1917)
MA
RI
CT
NV (1914)
UT (1896)
NE
IA
MI (1918)
PA
NJ
DE
CA (1911)
CO (1893)
KS (1912)
MO
IL IN OH
WV VA
MD
DC
AZ (1912)
NM
OK (1918)
AR
KY
TN
NC
SC
TX
LA
MS AL GA
FL

▯▯▯ Full suffrage, with year voted

▨ Partial woman suffrage (1913–1920)

▯ No statewide woman suffrage

1 **Based on the map, which state would be *most* likely to ratify the Nineteenth Amendment?**

   A Florida

   B New York

   C Pennsylvania

   D Virginia

2 **Which statement *best* describes suffrage between 1913 and 1920?**

   A Wyoming was the only state that had passed it.

   B Most states gave women at least partial suffrage.

   C Most states gave women full suffrage.

   D None of the states had passed it.

3 **In 1890, the National American Woman Suffrage Association**

   A formed a national strategy to pass woman suffrage.

   B split into two groups that disagreed about how to gain suffrage.

   C held a convention in Seneca Falls.

   D prevented men from voting in many states.

4 ***Most* women who worked outside of the home in the late 1800s and early 1900s did so because**

   A they were better educated.

   B men were fighting a war.

   C they wanted equal rights.

   D of economic need.

Name _____ Date _____

REVIEW

CALIFORNIA CONTENT STANDARD 11.5.5   *The Harlem Renaissance*

Specific Objective: Describe the Harlem Renaissance and new trends in literature, music, and art, with special attention to the work of writers.

Read the summary to answer the questions on the next page.

Background

- Communities of African Americans grew in northern cities during the Great Migration from the South during the early 1900s. Harlem, a neighborhood in upper Manhattan in New York City, was the largest and most important.

- A middle class of educated and successful African Americans had emerged in the cities in the early 1900s. Many lived in Harlem.

- Groups such as Marcus Garvey's "back-to-Africa" movement and work by the National Association for the Advancement of Colored People (NAACP) helped African Americans feel pride in themselves and their unique culture.

- African-American efforts during World War I brought some recognition from whites. However, lynchings and race riots were common after the war.

- The economy through the 1920s was generally strong and people had money to spend on entertainment, books, and art.

Harlem Renaissance

- A renaissance is a time when art, literature, and learning become important again.

- As writers, artists, and musicians in Harlem created outstanding works, the period from about 1920 through the early 1930s became know as the Harlem Renaissance.

- The Harlem Renaissance allowed many African Americans to experience these new works. White society first became aware of African-American writers and artists during this period and began to show appreciation for their work.

- Many of the creators were friends and their works inspired one another.

- There was no single style of writing, music, or art during the time. Writers focused on African Americans and their experiences in life, including facing acism and injustice.

Leading Writers, Musicians, and Artists

- Langston Hughes was the most famous poet of the time. His poems focused on the lives of working class African Americans.

- Zora Neale Hurston collected African-American folklore and tales. Some characters in her novels were women searching for identity and community.

- Ragtime and blues music were combined with other influences to create a unique style, which came to be called "jazz." Duke Ellington, Louis Armstrong, and Jelly Roll Morton were instrumental leaders and Bessie Smith and others sang. Whites came to famous Harlem clubs to hear the music.

Name _____ Date _____

PRACTICE

CALIFORNIA CONTENT
STANDARD 11.5.5   *The Harlem Renaissance*

Directions: Choose the letter of the *best* answer.

1 Which factor was *most* important
   in the development of the Harlem
   Renaissance?

   A government support for African-
      American artists

   B the promotion of black pride by
      African-American leaders

   C large communities of African
      Americans in Southern cities

   D African Americans receiving
      scholarships to art school

2 The Harlem Renaissance lasted
   from about

   A 1900 until the start of World War I
      (1914).

   B 1910 until the start of World War II
      (1941).

   C 1920 until the Great Depression
      (early 1930s).

   D 1929 until the start of World War II
      (1941).

3 How did the Harlem Renaissance
   affect white society?

   A Whites dismissed the work of African
      Americans as too limited.

   B Whites prevented African-American
      books from being sold in the South.

   C Whites began to appreciate African-
      American writers and artists.

   D Whites had no awareness of the
      movement.

4 Zora Neale Hurston called poor
   Southern blacks with little schooling
   "the greatest cultural wealth of the
   continent." Her outlook led her to
   write

   A plays about Southern blacks who
      had become rich.

   B stories that celebrated women
      searching for their identity.

   C poems about the way slavery
      oppressed Southern blacks.

   D songs based on spirituals sung in
      Southern churches.

5 Which type of artistic expression
   brought *most* white people to
   Harlem?

   A art galleries

   B "jazz" music shows

   C poetry readings

   D public sculpture

6 Writers during the Harlem
   Renaissance

   A developed a single consistent style
      of writing.

   B focused on African-American
      experiences.

   C wrote about white society and how
      it needed to change.

   D used a style most popular in the
      early 1800s.

REVIEW

CALIFORNIA CONTENT
STANDARD 11.5.6

The Spread of Popular Culture

Specific Objective: Trace the growth and effects of radio and movies and their role in the worldwide diffusion of popular culture.

Read the summary to answer the questions on the next page.

American Life in the 1920s

- Labor reforms and union activities achieved shorter working hours for industrial workers. Americans had more leisure time and took up many new types of hobbies.
- During most of the decade, people had more money to spend than previous years. They spent it on consumer goods as well as entertainment.

The Rise of Radio

- Wireless radio communication was still being developed in the early 1900s.
- Radios were used for military reasons during World War I and private radios banned.
- Radio manufacturers tried ways to increase personal radio sales after the war. Westinghouse Electric started a commercial radio station in 1920 in Pittsburgh. Programs included recorded music, news, and sports scores without commercials.
- The station was so successful that other radio manufacturers, such as General Electric (GE) and Radio Corporation of America (RCA), started stations in New York and other areas. People quickly bought radios so they could listen.
- There were about 60,000 home radios in the United States in 1922. The number increased to 3 million in 1924, 10 million by 1930, and 20 million by 1934.
- Stations began raising money with paid commercials. By the mid-1930s, radio was a $100 million business.
- Large networks such as National Broadcasting Company (NBC) and Columbia Broadcast System (CBS) formed to link stations across the country. They linked these stations so they could all broadcast some of the same programs.
- Radio provided a link between people in different areas of the country. People in rural and urban areas, and in the North, South and West could all hear the same sports event or radio comedy or drama. They could learn about news as it happened.
- Entertainment shared by many came to be known as popular culture.

Motion Pictures

- Movies in the early 1900s were silent. Musicians played music in theaters while they were shown. Any dialogue was provided by printed words on the screen.
- Millions went to silent movies as an escape from everyday life. Stars of comedies and romances influenced fashions and were covered in fan magazines.
- "Talkies" brought sound to motion pictures in 1927 in *The Jazz Singer*. Mickey Mouse was the first cartoon to speak in 1928. Soon all movies had sound. Movie attendance doubled in just three years.
- Like radio, movies allowed people across the country to share popular culture.

Name _____   Date _____

PRACTICE

CALIFORNIA CONTENT
STANDARD 11.5.6

*The Spread of
Popular Culture*

Directions: Choose the letter of the *best* answer.

1   Which statement describes life for *most* Americans during the 1920s?

  A They worked more hours than previously and had more money to spend.

  B They worked fewer hours than previously and had more money to spend.

  C They worked fewer hours than previously but had less money to spend.

  D They worked more hours than previously but had less money to spend.

2   During World War I, radios were

  A restricted to military purposes.

  B used to broadcast news of the war.

  C first used for paid commercials.

  D used to rally support for the war.

3   Radio stations were first intended to

  A provide emergency communications between cities.

  B provide education to their listeners.

  C increase radio sales for manufacturers.

  D help the government broadcast news.

4   Why were large radio networks like NBC and CBS formed?

  A to force small local companies to contribute to national broadcasts

  B to compete with radio stations owned by radio manufacturers

  C to link stations across the country to allow for common programming

  D to allow more people to own radio stations in their communities

5   How did people react to "talkies?"

  A Movies with sound weren't successful for almost ten years.

  B People were disappointed in how stars spoke and sang.

  C People preferred silent movies with live music.

  D Movie attendance doubled in only three years.

6   How did radio and movies help establish a national popular culture?

  A People in different areas and living conditions could share common entertainment.

  B Radio and movie prices were so high, only rich people could afford them.

  C Radio and movie characters always portrayed people in the middle and lower classes.

  D Radio and movies had little impact on building a national popular culture.

Name _____   Date _____

Technology Changes America

Specific Objective: Describe the rise of mass production techniques, the growth of cities, the impact of new technologies, and the resulting prosperity and effect on the American landscape.

Read the charts to answer the questions on the next page.

Changes in the Early 1900s
• **Mass production**—Henry Ford and other industrialists used assembly lines to increase the speed of production. For example, Ford reduced the time it took to produce one car from about twelve hours in 1910 to about two hours in 1913. By the 1920s, many goods were produced much faster than previously.
• **New transportation**—Electric streetcars helped people travel within cities. Cars quickly became popular—by the late 1920s about one in every five Americans owned one. Mail delivery by air began in 1918 and commercial passenger flights in 1927.
• **Expansion of cities**—Cities grew along with the expansion of industry. The automobile industry led to the growth of new cities built around related industries.
• **Electricity**—Factories used electricity to power machines and light their buildings. Factories no longer needed to be located near waterpower. New technology allowed electricity to be more easily transmitted over a distance, meaning that homes away from the center of cities could have electric lights and appliances.

Effects on the Economy and Landscape
• **General prosperity**—The 1920s was generally a time of prosperity. Improved technologies helped factories produce more goods and workers earn more money. Faster production made goods less expensive. Many people bought goods on credit.
• **Roads**—Growth in the number of automobiles led to the need for better roads. In 1916, the federal government began to pay half of the cost of highways built by states. By 1930, most major cities in the United States were connected by paved roads. Trucks competed with railroads to deliver goods. Roadside businesses such as gas stations, motels, and restaurants sprang up.
• **Changes in cities**—Improvements in construction techniques and materials made skyscrapers possible. Skyscrapers allowed cities to make better use of land and allowed more people to live and work in less space. Changes in transportation allowed cities to grow outward into suburbs. People lived farther away from work or other services because they could travel more easily. This expansion away from the center is sometimes called urban sprawl.

PRACTICE

**CALIFORNIA CONTENT
STANDARD 11.5.7**

Technology Changes America

Directions: Choose the letter of the *best* answer.

1 How did mass production techniques change industry in the early 1900s?

  A They made factory jobs more interesting for the workers.

  B They made home appliances more expensive.

  C They allowed industry to produce more goods more quickly.

  D They led to growth in custom-built products.

2 What was the *main* reason that people began to live farther from the center of cities in the early 1900s?

  A They needed larger homes for consumer goods like refrigerators.

  B They wanted to use the land for growing food.

  C They could travel to work and other services more easily.

  D Better jobs were located in the suburbs.

3 Which statement *best* describes the growth in auto sales during the early 1900s?

  A Sales grew very quickly once cars were mass produced.

  B Sales didn't increase greatly until after the Great Depression.

  C Sales were slow and steady throughout the 1920s.

  D Sales didn't increase until Ford started offering cars in different colors.

4 Which statement describes how electricity affected industry in the early 1900s?

  A Electricity was so costly to use that it drove up prices.

  B Factories used electricity to power their machines and produce more goods.

  C Electricity was seldom used because coal was so cheap.

  D Factories tried to use electricity for their machines but it proved too dangerous.

5 Which statement *best* describes urban sprawl?

  A the growth of cities away from their centers

  B the movement of people into cities from rural areas

  C the reduction in population density in suburbs

  D the tendency for new cities to support the auto industry

6 How had the automobile affected the American landscape by 1930?

  A More people lived in central cities that had good parking.

  B The automobile encouraged the growth of small towns.

  C Paved auto roads connected most major American cities.

  D The landscape was basically the same as it had been in 1900.

Name _____ Date _____

CALIFORNIA CONTENT
STANDARD 11.6.1

Money and the Economy

Specific Objective: Describe the monetary issues of the late nineteenth and early twentieth centuries that gave rise to the establishment of the Federal Reserve and the weaknesses in key sectors of the economy in the late 1920s.

Read the summary to answer questions on the next page.

Establishing the Federal Reserve System

- Through the late 1800s, banks often closed during economic crises. The federal government or the banking system could not increase the supply of money or credit. People lost what they deposited, and paper money could not be exchanged for gold.
- Crises in 1873, 1883, and 1893 caused many banks to fail and businesses to go bankrupt. After a huge bank failed in 1907, Congress came up with a plan.
- The Federal Reserve System was established in 1913 under President Wilson.
- The Federal Reserve System still functions today to prevent bank failures and regulate the supply of money.

A Weak Economy That Seemed Strong

From the beginning of World War I in 1914 until 1929, everyone believed the U.S. economy was stronger than it had ever been. But during the late 1920s, problems in the economy began to build up. Before the stock market crashed in 1929, the U.S. economy had the following problems:

Uneven distribution of wealth—The richest people got richer while workers' wages increased only slightly. With only a small increase in their income, most people couldn't afford to buy all of the products of U.S. industry.

Too much production with too little demand—Factories continued to produce more and more goods, but people could not afford them. Warehouses were filled with unsold goods. Most major industries had slowed down by the middle of 1929.

Widespread use of credit—People began to buy goods on credit. Many owed more money than they could pay back. By the end of the 1920s, buying slowed.

Stock speculation—Because it seemed the stock market would always keep rising, many people borrowed money to buy stocks. If the stocks did not rise, those who had borrowed would not have the money to pay for them.

Farm problems—Farmers had problems as soon as the war ended. Many had borrowed money to buy more land and grow more crops. After the war, European farmers started producing again, and prices dropped for American farm products. The government did not help farmers, and many lost their farms.

Weak industries—Older industries such as iron, railroads, mining, and textiles did not share in the general prosperity.

International economic problems—The United States kept tariffs high on foreign goods to protect U.S. industries. However, if foreign countries could not sell goods in the United States, they could not afford to buy U.S. exports or to pay back loans.

PRACTICE

CALIFORNIA CONTENT
STANDARD 11.6.1

Money and the Economy

Directions: Choose the letter of the *best* answer.

1 Why did banks often close in economic crises through the late 1800s?

A Banks did not loan out enough money, so they did not make much on interest.

B Gold mines closed down and there was not enough gold to exchange for paper money.

C There was no national system to increase the supply of money or credit.

D Banks and railroads were commonly owned, and when railroads had trouble, banks closed.

2 Which statement *best* describes the Federal Reserve System?

A It was established in 1913 and lasted until the stock market crash of 1929.

B It let private bankers control the economy through the interest rates on loans.

C It was established in 1913 and continues to regulate the money supply today.

D It was established in 1913 and backed U.S. currency with silver.

3 By the end of the 1920s, buying slowed because

A most people refused to borrow so they could buy more.

B most people owed more money than they could afford to pay back.

C most people preferred to save money, rather than spend it.

D most people believed there would be another world war.

4 During the 1920s, U.S. farmers

A got help from the federal government to repay their debts.

B enjoyed the booming economy like many others.

C continued to find a good market in Europe for their products.

D suffered from low prices and too much debt.

5 How did high U.S. tariffs affect the economy during the 1920s?

A Factories increased production to keep up with the demand for U.S. exports.

B Foreign countries could not afford to buy U.S. exports or repay U.S. loans.

C Prices for U.S. goods were kept high, so fewer people could afford to buy them.

D U.S. companies fought tariffs because they believed in open markets.

6 Which statement describes the way wealth was distributed during the 1920s?

A Workers gained at a much higher rate than owners or the middle class.

B The middle class gained much more than the owners or workers.

C The richest people got much richer while working wages rose only slightly.

D Owners did not have enough to invest in new businesses.

REVIEW

CALIFORNIA CONTENT
STANDARD 11.6.2

Responses to the Great Depression

Specific Objective: Understand the explanations of the principal causes of the Great Depression and the steps taken by the Federal Reserve, Congress, and Presidents Herbert Hoover and Franklin Delano Roosevelt to combat the economic crisis.

Read the information to answer questions on the next page.

Causes of the Great Depression
- Tariffs and war debt policies cut down the foreign market for U.S. goods.
- A crisis in the farm sector led to falling prices and increased debt.
- The Federal Reserve kept interest rates low and encouraged borrowing that led to excessive debt.
- An unequal distribution of income led to falling demand for consumer goods.
- People bought stocks on credit, which meant huge losses when stocks did not rise.
- The stock market crash fueled a financial panic.

Hoover and Congress Respond (1929–1932)
- Initial inaction—tried to let economy fix itself
- Tried to convince businesses to invest—unsuccessful because of huge business losses
- Cut government spending and raised taxes tried to balance budget but made problems worse
- Congress increased tariffs—tried to protect U.S. businesses, but when other countries did the same, exports and demand for goods dropped.
- Federal Reserve—lent money to banks and allowed interest rates to drop in 1930, but in 1931 it did not do enough to keep banks from failing.

Roosevelt's New Deal (1932–1940)
Relief for Needy People
- Jobs programs decreased unemployment (though it remained high until World War II).
- Provided loans to protect people's homes; Provided direct relief to people through state and federal programs to help unemployed, aged, and ill

Economic Recovery
- Tried to lower production to meet demand
- Assisted farmers by helping raise prices (paid them to destroy products and leave land unplanted)
- Regulated industry with rules for production, fair competition, and worker pay and conditions
- Increased money in economy through huge jobs programs and public building projects

Financial Reform
- Restored faith in banks by closing them until they were inspected and found to be in order
- The Federal Reserve Act created the Federal Deposit Insurance Corporation to protect people's money deposited in banks.
- Supported regulation of stock market to prevent false information and financial gains to insiders with special information

PRACTICE

CALIFORNIA CONTENT
STANDARD 11.6.2

Responses to the
Great Depression

Directions: Choose the letter of the *best* answer.

1 How did the Federal Reserve affect investment in the stock market during *most* of the 1920s?

A It controlled the money supply, so only the wealthy could invest in stocks.

B It successfully controlled banks that wanted to speculate in stocks.

C It kept interest rates low, and people borrowed money to invest in stocks.

D It regulated companies that wanted to make money by selling stock.

2 What was the result of raising tariffs after the Depression had begun?

A It helped protect U.S. businesses.

B Other countries did the same thing and exports dropped.

C Farmers could sell their goods overseas for higher prices.

D It had little effect on the U.S. and international economies.

3 What was the reaction of President Hoover and Congress when the Great Depression first began?

A They did not take action because they believed the economy could fix itself.

B They cut taxes and increased spending to increase the money supply.

C They offered to help workers who had lost their jobs.

D They forced businesses to hire back workers who had lost their jobs.

4 How did President Roosevelt help farmers during the Great Depression?

A He started a program to ship farm products to where they were needed.

B He set up factories in farming areas so farmers could work at other jobs.

C He created a government agency to buy their farms at a reasonable price.

D He paid farmers to destroy some crops and leave fields unplanted.

5 To help boost industry, Roosevelt

A encouraged foreign companies to invest in American businesses.

B established rules for industrial production, working conditions, and competition.

C removed regulations that cost businesses too much money.

D had the government buy many products so that factories could be successful.

6 Which statement *best* describes ways Roosevelt's policies worked for financial reform?

A They regulated the stock market and eliminated taxes on corporations.

B They inspected and regulated banks and regulated the stock market.

C They eliminated the Federal Reserve System to make banks stronger.

D They gave the Federal Reserve System control over corporate profits.

Name _____ Date _____

**CALIFORNIA CONTENT
STANDARD 11.6.3**

Human Toll of the Depression

Specific Objective: Describe the human toll of the Depression, natural disasters, and unwise agricultural practices and their effect on the depopulation of rural regions and on political movements of the left and right, with particular attention to the Dust Bowl refugees and their social and economic impacts in California.

Read the diagram to answer questions on the next page.

The Great Depression

The Human Toll

- People in cities lost their jobs and homes, lived in shantytowns, and got food from soup kitchens and bread lines.
- People in rural areas lost their land and homes. Some grew food for themselves.
- Families suffered as men wandered the country looking for work. Women worked for low wages and had too little food at home. Children's health suffered and many left school or left home to look for work.
- African-American unemployment was more than 50% compared to 25% for others. Latinos were targeted for attacks and deportation.

The Dust Bowl

- To grow more crops, farmers removed grass and trees from huge areas of the Great Plains from Canada to Mexico. The land was quickly exhausted and became useless for much farming.
- A drought for several years in the early 1930s turned soil to dust. High winds at the same time blew dust for hundreds of miles.
- Many farmers lost farms because of low crop prices and huge debts.
- Hundreds of thousands of people packed their belongings and left for California to look for work. The influx of workers drove wages down and strained social services in the state. Migrants had little experience mixing with the minorities in California. In addition, many Californians looked down on the migrants, calling them "Okies."

Political Movements and the New Deal

- On the right, the American Liberty League said New Deal programs spent too much on direct relief and interfered with the free-market economy.
- On the left, Father Charles Coughlin, Dr. Francis Townsend, and Huey Long all opposed the New Deal. They said it didn't help people enough. They favored greater government support.
- Minorities (African Americans and Mexican Americans) generally benefited less from the New Deal and became more politically active.
- Roosevelt created the New Deal coalition that brought many groups together in support of the Democratic Party. Labor unions, whites in the South, urban groups, and African Americans supported the party for many years.

PRACTICE

CALIFORNIA CONTENT
STANDARD 11.6.3

Human Toll of the Depression

Directions: Choose the letter of the *best* answer.

1 Which statement *best* describes opponents of the New Deal?

   A They all thought its programs did not help people enough.

   B They all thought its programs did not respect individual rights and property.

   C They were mostly religious groups that opposed it on moral grounds.

   D Critics of the New Deal existed on both the left and the right.

2 Which statement *best* describes the human toll of the Great Depression?

   A Problems were greatest in cities and for whites.

   B People in the rural South and West had the greatest problems.

   C All types of people suffered in all areas of the country.

   D Women had fewer problems because they did not lose their jobs.

3 The Dust Bowl was caused by

   A New Deal farm policies.

   B drought, winds, and poor farming practices.

   C farmers using too much fertilizer.

   D farmers losing their savings in the stock market.

4 How did the New Deal coalition affect politics in the United States?

   A It brought together a variety of groups that supported the Democratic Party.

   B It was successful in mounting a conservative opposition to the New Deal.

   C It fought against the power of labor unions and rights for African Americans.

   D It had little effect on politics because most of its members did not vote.

5 How did the New Deal affect minority groups?

   A New Deal programs helped minorities more than other groups.

   B Minority groups became more politically active during the New Deal.

   C Most minorities joined the Republicans in opposing the New Deal.

   D Minorities preferred to rely on churches rather than government help.

6 *Most* victims of the Dust Bowl moved to

   A California.

   B Canada and Mexico.

   C the Great Plains.

   D the Southeast.

Name _____   Date _____

REVIEW

CALIFORNIA CONTENT
STANDARD 11.6.4

New Deal Economic Policies

Specific Objective: Analyze the effects of and the controversies arising from the New Deal economic policies and the expanded role of the federal government in society and the economy since the 1930s.

Read the diagram to answer questions on the next page.

Labor Relations
- The Wagner Act established rights of workers to organize and join unions. The National Labor Relations Board (NLRB) required companies to treat unions fairly and to bargain with them.
- Fair Labor Standards Act set maximum hours and minimum pay for most workers.
- Opponents said programs gave too much power to unions. Controversy arose in late 1940s and 1950s over union and employer rights.

Water and Energy Development
- Tennessee Valley Authority (TVA) was established to build dams and produce power using Tennessee River. The project brought power to rural areas and protected against floods.
- Central Valley Project in California provided water for irrigation and urban use.
- Opponents said government programs were unfair competition for private business.

New Deal Programs

Public Works and Jobs
- Civilian Conservation Corps (CCC) provided jobs for millions of unemployed youth building parks and maintaining national forests to protect the natural environment.
- Public Works Administration (PWA) and Works Progress Administration (WPA) targeted employment. Millions of skilled and unskilled workers helped build dams, bridges, highways, and schools. The programs also employed writers and artists.
- Opponents said work was "make work" that was not needed.

Farm Programs
- Agricultural Adjustment Act (AAA) paid farmers to leave land unplanted and destroy some crops and products to reduce supply and raise prices.
- Programs were created to provide loans to tenant and small farmers to buy land.
- Opponents said destroying food was wrong when many people were hungry.

Social Welfare
- The Social Security Act established old-age pension for retired workers. It also provided unemployment assistance and aid for children and the disabled.
- Social Security still functions as a safety net for millions of elderly and disabled. Some reform is needed to help the system pay promised benefits in the future.

Name _____ Date _____

PRACTICE

CALIFORNIA CONTENT
STANDARD 11.6.4

New Deal Economic Policies

Directions: Choose the letter of the *best* answer.

1 New Deal labor policies and programs generally

  A limited safety rules and inspections that cost businesses money.

  B supported owners' rights to prevent unions from representing workers.

  C supported fair labor practices, including a minimum wage for workers.

  D established rules to limit options for women and African Americans to work.

2 The WPA and the CCC programs showed Roosevelt's belief in

  A creating government jobs to get people back to work.

  B providing loans to businesses to retrain unemployed workers.

  C employing only unskilled workers in public works programs.

  D supporting private businesses to hire unskilled workers.

3 New Deal farm programs were designed to reduce supply and raise prices. Opponents objected because they thought

  A food should be sold overseas where prices were higher.

  B farm problems could be solved if farmers used better techniques.

  C the country needed low food prices to compete with foreign farm products.

  D it was wrong to limit production of food when many people were hungry.

4 Projects like the Tennessee Valley Authority and Central Valley Project in California

  A were strongly supported by members of the business community.

  B were never completed because of a lack of skilled workers.

  C harnessed natural resources to improve the quality of life in those areas.

  D forced large landowners to give up many acres of valuable land.

5 Social Security was established during the New Deal to provide pensions for retired workers. It also provided

  A assistance for children and disabled people.

  B age requirements for public schools.

  C guidelines for medical care for workers.

  D jobs for unemployed youth.

6 How did the New Deal affect government's role in the economy?

  A Government took steps to deregulate key industries.

  B Government took a more active role in managing the economy.

  C Government adopted a hands off policy for most sectors of the economy.

  D Government's role in the economy remained unchanged by the New Deal.

Name _____ Date _____

The Labor Movement

Specific Objective: Trace the advances and retreats of organized labor, from the creation of the American Federation of Labor and the Congress of Industrial Organizations to current issues of a postindustrial, multinational economy, including the United Farm Workers in California.

Read the sequence diagram to answer questions on the next page.

American Federation of Labor (AFL)
- The first lasting and effective group of labor unions, formed in 1886
- Made up of separate unions of skilled workers for different trades
- Mostly concerned with specific issues such as shorter hours and higher pay

Struggles in the Early 1900s
- Greater industrialization led to larger unions and more strikes.
- International Workers of the World (IWW) was small but led many strikes. Their radical politics led owners and politicians to label them communists and anarchists. Labor struggles were often violent.
- New government rules protected unions, but several large strikes were lost and union strength declined in 1920s.

The New Deal
- New Deal acts guaranteed workers' rights to unionize.
- Union membership grew rapidly to record highs, about 10 million in 1941.
- Congress of Industrial Organizations (CIO) left the AFL in 1938. Its goal was to organize workers in industries such as steel, automobiles, and shipping.

Struggles After World War II
- After World War II, there were many strikes. Congress passed the Taft-Hartley Act that limited the rights of unions.
- AFL and CIO merged to become AFL-CIO in 1955. It faced problems of some union leaders gaining money and power illegally.

United Farm Workers
- Migrant farm workers in California had never been unionized and suffered low pay, poor conditions, and few benefits.
- César Chávez and Dolores Huerta formed United Farm Workers (UFW) in 1966.
- Chávez led a national grape boycott. Years later, growers accepted the union.

A Global Economy
- Total union membership in 2003 was about 16 million workers, about 13 percent of workers. Membership has steadily declined since 1983.
- Unions are not strong in a global economy where companies can move jobs to other areas of the country or to foreign countries.
- Only about 8 percent of private sector workers are in unions, compared to about 37 percent of governmental workers.

PRACTICE

CALIFORNIA CONTENT
STANDARD 11.6.5

The Labor Movement

Directions: Choose the letter of the *best* answer.

1 Which union is *both* the oldest and the longest lasting?

  A American Federation of Labor (AFL)

  B Congress of Industrial Organizations (CIO)

  C Industrial Workers of the World (IWW)

  D United Farm Workers (UFW)

2 How did the growth of industry in the early 1900s affect union membership?

  A Union membership grew and there were more strikes.

  C Union membership fell because employers were paying higher wages.

  B The IWW became the largest union in the country.

  D Union membership fell because laws prevented workers from joining.

3 How did the New Deal respond to unions during the Great Depression?

  A Workers could join unions but the unions could not strike.

  B Employers could decide if a union was best for its workers.

  C Workers could join existing unions but could not organize new ones.

  D Workers were guaranteed the right to organize unions.

4 After World War II, the Taft-Hartley Act

  A made unions illegal for police and other public employees.

  B prosecuted corrupt labor leaders.

  C recognized the CIO as the only group that could organize labor unions.

  D limited the rights of unions.

5 To win the right to negotiate with growers, the United Farm Workers

  A led strikes by workers in the Midwest.

  B damaged farm fields and equipment.

  C opposed other unions in California.

  D led a national boycott of grapes.

6 Which problem do unions face in today's global economy?

  A Employers in the United States no longer have to follow labor laws.

  B Employers can move companies to another area or a foreign country.

  C Workers refuse to move around the country to get jobs.

  D The minimum wage is so high that most workers feel comfortable with their pay.

Name _____ Date _____

REVIEW

CALIFORNIA CONTENT STANDARD 11.7.1

America Enters World War II

Specific Objective: Examine the origins of American involvement in the war, with an emphasis on the events that precipitated the attack on Pearl Harbor.

Read the chart to answer questions on the next page.

Year	Events	U.S. and Allied Responses
1930– 1936	• Militarists, dictators in control in Japan, Germany, Italy	• Isolationism in United States—desire to stay out of European conflicts
1937	• Japan attacks China again.	• United States supports China with supplies and arms (China not formally at war).
1938	• Germany takes Austria.	• France and Great Britain try to appease Germany with Munich Pact.
1939	• Germany and USSR sign nonaggression pact. • Germany takes Czechoslovakia and Poland; USSR takes part of Poland.	• United States announces neutrality. • U.S. approves cash-and-carry system to provide arms and supplies to allies who used their own ships for transport.
1940	• Germany takes France. • Germany attacks Great Britain. • Germany, Italy, and Japan join as Axis powers. • Germany attacks U.S. and British supply convoys.	• United States announces it will provide all aid short of war to allies. • U.S. begins military draft. • U.S. increases defense spending.
1941	• Germany attacks USSR. • German submarines continue attacks on U.S. supply ships. • Japan increases its attacks in Asia, taking French colonies. • United States and Japan enter peace talks about Asia while Japan plans attack on United States. • Japan attacks Pearl Harbor. • Germany and Italy declare war on United States.	• United States begins Lend-Lease plan to supply arms and supplies to Great Britain and USSR without immediate payment. • U.S. Navy authorized to attack any German submarines on sight—U.S. in undeclared war with Germany • U.S. cuts off oil supplies to Japan. • U.S. knows Japan will attack, but not when and where; U.S. continues preparing for war with Japan and in Europe. • U.S. declares war on Japan. • United States formally at war with Germany and Italy; becomes an ally of Great Britain, France, and USSR

PRACTICE

CALIFORNIA CONTENT STANDARD 11.7.1

America Enters World War II

Directions: Choose the letter of the *best* answer.

1 How did the United States respond to the rise of militarists and dictators in Japan, Germany, and Italy *before* 1937?

  A It offered economic aid to the militarists and dictators.

  B It built up its military forces and offered arms to threatened nations.

  C It joined the League of Nations to prevent these leaders from getting too strong.

  D It tried to remain isolated from European conflicts.

2 The cash-and-carry system of 1939 allowed the United States to

  A sell war materials to allies as long as they paid cash and transported the goods themselves.

  B buy imports from Germany and France as long as payments were made in cash.

  C increase production of arms as long as they were paid for when ordered.

  D prevent Germany from buying U.S. arms by demanding repayment of loans.

3 By 1941, the United States was in an undeclared war with Germany because

  A the Air Force had begun bombing targets in Europe.

  B the Navy was authorized to shoot at German submarines.

  C ground troops were preparing to land in Europe.

  D some of the fighting in Africa involved U.S. troops.

4 At the time of the attack on Pearl Harbor in 1941, the United States and Japan

  A shared control of naval bases in Hawaii.

  B were involved in peace talks concerning conflicts in Asia.

  C had engaged in several naval battles in the Pacific.

  D had not formally contacted each other for several years.

5 Which of these events was the *most immediate* cause of Japan's attack on Pearl Harbor?

  A Japan took control of Manchuria in China.

  B Japan joined the Axis powers of Germany and Italy.

  C The United States cut off oil sales to Japan.

  D The United States refused to negotiate with Japan.

6 In 1940, the United States decided it would provide "all aid short of war" to allies after

  A Japan took French colonies in Asia.

  B the USSR took part of Poland.

  C Great Britain and France tried to appease Hitler.

  D Germany took France and attacked Great Britain.

Name _____ Date _____

Allied Strategy in World War II

Specific Objective: Understand U.S. and Allied wartime strategy, including the major battles of Midway, Normandy, Iwo Jima, Okinawa, and the Battle of the Bulge.

Read the summary to answer questions on the next page.

Overall Allied Strategy

- Allies at serious disadvantage when United States enters war in late 1941— France under German control, Great Britain still under attack, USSR fighting German invasion, Northern Africa under German and Italian control.
- Allies decide war in Europe must be won first.
- Attacks in North Africa and Italy 1942–1943 brought some Allied success.
- War in Pacific (U.S. vs. Japan) would not be first priority until victory in Europe.

Normandy • June 6, 1944

A total of 3 million troops from United States, Canada, and Great Britain. Invasion of Normandy was largest land-sea-air operation in military history—called D-Day. German resistance strong. Allies held while more troops landed; after one month 1 million troops in France. Paris liberated in August and all of France taken from Germany by September.

Battle of the Bulge • December 16, 1944–January 21, 1945

Allied troops advanced east towards Germany in late 1944. Germany launched surprise counterattack in December. German troops penetrated into Allied territory and created a "bulge" in Allied lines. After month of furious battles, Allies pushed back bulge to previous line. German losses severe and Germans retreated for remainder of war.

Midway • June, 1942

Japan took Pacific islands, Southeast Asia, Philippines, much of China by early 1942. Allies prevented attack on Australia. Allies destroyed Japanese planes and ships before they could attack Midway. Severe Japanese losses a turning point in Pacific; Allies moved to take back islands.

Iwo Jima • February–March, 1945

Allies used strategy of island hopping to take back Philippines and other islands. Iwo Jima very important as a fueling spot. More than 6,000 marines died taking the island.

Okinawa • April–June, 1945

Last obstacle before Allied assult on Japan. Fighting lasted almost 3 months. Number of casualties raised questions about costs of invading Japan.

PRACTICE

CALIFORNIA CONTENT
STANDARD 11.7.2

*Allied Strategy in
World War II*

Directions: Choose the letter of the *best* answer.

1 The *first* priority of the Allies, once the United States entered World War II, was winning the war in

A Europe.

B the Pacific.

C Russia.

D Southeast Asia.

2 What was the immediate result of the invasion of Normandy?

A Allied losses prevented them from continuing their attacks for several months.

B Paris and all of France were liberated from Germany within a few months.

C Germany increased its air attacks against Great Britain.

D German losses were so severe that they retreated for the remainder of the war.

3 Why was the Battle of the Bulge important to the Allied strategy?

A It was the first Allied victory on the European continent since the fall of France.

B It was the beginning of the combined Allied assault on Japan.

C It marked the last significant attack by the Germans against the Allies.

D It showed the superiority of Allied air power in the Pacific.

4 The Battle of Midway was a turning point in the war in the Pacific because

A it was the first time Japan had used aircraft carriers to launch an attack.

B General MacArthur returned as he had promised he would.

C both sides realized there was little hope for victory.

D heavy Japanese losses allowed the Allies to begin retaking Pacific islands.

5 The battle of Okinawa affected Allied plans for the war by

A leading the Allies to abandon their strategy of "island hopping."

B forcing the Allies to wait until the USSR could fight in the Pacific.

C shifting the Allied strategy from a ground war to an air war.

D making the Allies consider the potential cost of an invasion of Japan.

6 The Battle of the Bulge began in 1944 when

A the Allies launched a surprise attack against advancing German troops.

B Germany successfully penetrated into Allied territory creating a "bulge."

C French troops weren't able to protect Paris after it had been liberated.

D Allied troops attacked a key port located at a "bulge" on the German coast.

Name _____ Date _____

REVIEW

CALIFORNIA CONTENT STANDARD 11.7.3

American Soldiers in World War II

Specific Objective: Identify the roles and sacrifices of individual American soldiers, as well as the unique contributions of the special fighting forces.

Read the summary to answer questions on the next page.

Volunteers and the Draft

- 5 million Americans volunteered for service but more were needed. They gave up jobs, families, and homes to serve.
- 10 million were drafted through the Selective Service system.
- Most received eight weeks of basic training before service.

Daily Life for Soldiers

- Life for combat soldiers was hard—food was often canned and cold, sleep might be on the ground or a cot, uniforms went unwashed, little communication with loved ones at home, constant danger of attack or sudden death.
- Support troops were needed for thousands of tasks, from driving supply trucks to typing reports; work often involved hard work, long hours, and monotonous jobs.

Decorated Heroes

- Millions earned a Purple Heart, awarded when a soldier is killed or injured in action.
- Officers like General Eisenhower and General MacArthur were honored for their planning and leadership.
- Soldiers like Audie Murphy were decorated for bravery; Murphy was given 24 medals by the United States and others from France and Belgium.

Special Fighting Forces

The U.S. Army was segregated during the war and kept some groups from combat. However, the following groups won many honors for their service.

- African Americans—about 1 million served, most limited to noncombat roles. Tuskegee Airmen (trained near Tuskegee, Alabama) became the first group of African-American pilots and won honors for service in Europe.
- Mexican Americans—more than 300,000 served, most in segregated units; Company E of 141st Regiment, 36th Division received a large number of medals
- Asian Americans—almost 50,000 served; the Japanese-American 442nd Regimental Combat Team became the most decorated unit in U.S. history.
- Native Americans—about 25,000 served; Navajo language served as an unbreakable code for U.S. troops fighting the Japanese. The Navajo Codetalkers were honored in 1969 for special contributions to the war effort.

Name _____   Date _____

PRACTICE

CALIFORNIA CONTENT
STANDARD 11.7.3

American Soldiers
in World War II

Directions: Choose the letter of the *best* answer.

1 **Which statement *best* describes how Americans felt about serving in the military during World War II?**

  A There were few volunteers because unemployment was low.

  B Large numbers volunteered in spite of the hardships they would face.

  C Most Americans were opposed to the war, and the entire army was drafted.

  D There was strong support for an all-volunteer army at that time.

2 **Combat soldiers in World War II often had**

  A little communication with loved ones at home.

  B fresh food that helped them stay healthy and ready to fight.

  C short tours of duty, generally limited to one year.

  D the best health care because so many doctors had enlisted.

3 **During World War II, millions received a Purple Heart, a medal which signifies that a soldier**

  A was a member of an elite special force.

  B has shown extreme bravery.

  C was injured or killed in action.

  D served in the Army Medical Corps.

4 **Which statement *best* describes integration in the U.S. military during World War II?**

  A There were few minorities in service because few volunteered.

  B Under Roosevelt's orders, it was the first army in history to be fully integrated.

  C Races were segregated, and minorities were often kept from combat roles.

  D Minorities served in the military but were not allowed outside the United States.

5 **African Americans during World War II**

  A were decorated as skilled pilots and soldiers.

  B made up almost half of all U.S. soldiers.

  C were only allowed to serve in the Navy.

  D refused to serve in support roles in the army.

6 **Thousands of Navajos distinguished themselves during World War II**

  A as scouts because of their excellent hunting and tracking skills.

  B in support roles as cooks because of their skills in cooking outdoors.

  C as aircraft gunners because of their excellent marksmanship.

  D by using their language as a code the Japanese could not break.

Name _____ Date _____

CALIFORNIA CONTENT
STANDARD 11.7.4   *Roosevelt's Foreign Policy*

Specific Objective: Analyze Roosevelt's foreign policy during World War II.

Read the sequence diagram to answer questions on the next page.

Isolationism and Neutrality

Congress and people in United States dedicated to staying out of wars like World War I.
United States tried to maintain neutrality as Hitler threatened Europe.

↓

Support for Democracies

After full-scale war began in Europe, Roosevelt established support for European democracies. Cash-and-carry and Lend-Lease programs provided arms and supplies.

↓

Four Freedoms

In January, 1941, Roosevelt identified goals for the world after the war. If world society
was based on Four Freedoms—Freedom of speech and expression; Freedom of worship;
Freedom from want; Freedom from fear—wars would not occur, because free countries
would cooperate. At the same time, Roosevelt pledged to help democracies fight.

↓

Atlantic Charter

Roosevelt and Churchill met in August 1941. Roosevelt pledged all assistance to Great
Britain and allies. Privately, Roosevelt promised to prepare for war and seek to force
entry into war. Atlantic Charter based on Four Freedoms. It states the right of everyone to
choose their own government, have access to natural resources, and be free from foreign
aggression. Agreement by other countries to charter in 1942 called Declaration of United
Nations and formed the basis for world organization called United Nations after war.

↓

Terms for Germany

Yalta Conference (February, 1945) established approach to Germany by Roosevelt,
Churchill, and Stalin after its defeat. Germany would be divided and controlled to prevent future military strength, war criminals prosecuted, and reparations paid. Roosevelt
accepted some of Stalins ideas to gain Stalin's support against Japan and for the United
Nations.

PRACTICE

CALIFORNIA CONTENT STANDARD 11.7.4

Roosevelt's Foreign Policy

Directions: Choose the letter of the *best* answer.

1 How did Roosevelt's foreign policy before the attack on Pearl Harbor reflect his ideas about neutrality?

  A He maintained strict neutrality until the attack by Japan.

  B He sold arms and supplies to Germany and Italy but not to Japan.

  C He did everything he could to support democratic governments.

  D He wanted to help the Allies but couldn't convince Congress to do so.

2 What was the *main* purpose of Roosevelt's Four Freedoms speech?

  A to set out a vision for a world in which war would be less likely

  B to provide hope for Americans who were still unemployed

  C to describe the reasons why the United States could not enter World War II

  D to prevent Japan from forming an alliance with Germany and Italy

3 The Atlantic Charter of August 1941 became the basis for

  A the Lend-Lease program.

  B the Munich Pact.

  C the United Nations.

  D the Neutrality Act.

4 How are the Four Freedoms speech and the Atlantic Charter related?

  A The Atlantic Charter was a German response to the Four Freedoms speech.

  B The Atlantic Charter reduced the Four Freedoms to a single statement of goals.

  C The Atlantic Charter was built on the ideas in the Four Freedoms speech.

  D The Four Freedoms referred to Japan and had no relation to the Atlantic Charter.

5 Roosevelt accepted some of Stalin's ideas during the Yalta Conference because

  A Stalin was ready to pull out of the war against Germany.

  B he needed Stalin's support in the war against Japan and for the United Nations.

  C Stalin's ideas were very similar to Churchill's.

  D the USSR was stronger than either the United States or Great Britain at that time.

6 After World War II, Roosevelt's policies continued to influence Japan. They encouraged Japan to

  A keep the same type of government as before.

  B prepare for war with Russia.

  C stay out of the United Nations.

  D establish a new democratic constitution.

Name _____ Date _____

REVIEW

CALIFORNIA CONTENT
STANDARD 11.7.5

The Home Front During World War II

Specific Objective: Understand the constitutional issues and impact of events on the U.S. home front, including the internment of Japanese Americans and the restrictions on German and Italian resident aliens; the response of the administration to Hitler's atrocities against Jews and other groups; the roles of women in military production; and the roles and growing demands of African Americans.

Read the summary to answer questions on the next page.

Internment of Japanese Americans

- In 1941, 120,000 Japanese Americans lived in United States, most on West Coast. Most were citizens; many Japanese Americans were serving in the army.

- In February, 1942, Roosevelt signed Executive Order 9066 on advice of the military requiring removal of people of Japanese ancestry from California and other areas.

- The army rounded up 110,000 people and interned them at prison camps (relocation centers). No specific charges were ever filed against them; there was no proof of sabotage. In 1944, the Supreme Court ruled internment legal for military necessity (*Korematsu* v. *United States.*) The decision is now considered a national embarrassment. In 1976, President Ford repealed Executive Order 9066.

Racial and Ethnic Tensions

- Race problems occurred throughout the war, with riots in summer of 1943. "Zoot-suit" riots occurred in Los Angeles between young Mexican Americans (wearing suits with baggy trousers and long coats) and white sailors and civilians. Riots in Detroit between African Americans and whites required federal troops.

- Nazis began attacks on Jews and others they considered inferior during late 1930s. German Jews tried to emigrate to escape. The United States and other countries stopped allowing Jewish immigration about 1939. Roosevelt refused further entry because the Depression was still strong and he didn't want more competition for jobs. Many Americans were anti-Semitic and feared plots by enemy agents.

Women at Work

- After proving their abilities, over 6 million women worked in defense industries. *Rosie the Riveter* was a symbol of women's abilities to do new types of jobs.

- Women were paid only about 60% of men's wages for doing the same job.

Some Progress for African Americans

- To avoid a huge protest march in 1944, Roosevelt signed an order for equal access to defense jobs.

- More than 2 million African Americans worked in defense industries, although many were limited to cleaning or other menial jobs.

Name _____   Date _____

The Home Front During World War II

Directions: Choose the letter of the *best* answer.

1 **What was the *main* constitutional issue raised by the Japanese internment during World War II?**

   A Illegal immigrants were deported without a hearing.

   B Asian immigrants were not allowed to become citizens.

   C American citizens were denied the right to hold peaceful protests.

   D American citizens were denied due process of law.

2 **Which *best* describes the Supreme Court decision handed down in *Korematsu* v. *United States* (1944)?**

   A It stated that persons of Japanese ancestry but born in the United States were not to be confined in relocation centers.

   B It declared the internment of Japanese Americans to be legal as a matter of military necessity.

   C It provided for financial compensation to Japanese for losses suffered during their confinement.

   D It repealed Roosevelt's executive order requiring the removal of Japanese Americans to internment camps.

3 **The United States suspended Jewish immigration around 1939. One reason was that**

   A other countries took them in.

   B the Supreme Court decided all new immigrants had to speak English.

   C there was fear of competition for jobs during the Depression.

   D they preferred to go to Canada.

4 **How did African Americans gain more access to defense industry jobs during World War II?**

   A General Eisenhower persuaded companies to hire them.

   B Roosevelt persuaded Congress to pass a bill that guaranteed equal access.

   C Roosevelt signed an order for equal access after they threatened a large protest.

   D Business leaders like Henry Ford showed other owners that equal access was a good policy.

5 **What did the African-American and Hispanic-American experiences during World War II have in common?**

   A increased racial hostilities

   B relocation to internment camps

   C widespread integration into American society

   D key roles and top positions in the American military

6 **American women who worked in defense industries during World War II performed**

   A more menial jobs than men but were paid more.

   B easier jobs than men, and were paid about equally.

   C the same jobs as men, and were paid about equally.

   D the same jobs as men but were paid less.

Name _____ Date _____

The War Affects Technology and Industry

Specific Objective: Describe major developments in aviation, weaponry, communication, and medicine and the war's impact on the location of American industry and use of resources.

Read the summary to answer questions on the next page.

Effects of World War II

Aviation

- The range, size, and speed of airplanes were increased greatly. U.S. and British air power were decisive factors in the defeat of Germany and Japan.
- Germany first developed jets for military use, as well as rocket-propelled planes.

Military Weapons

- Infrared technology was developed to allow soldiers to see in the dark.
- Because of the importance of air power, huge aircraft carriers were developed.
- The development of the atomic bomb affected warfare and foreign relations. Beginning with the Cold War, the threat of total destruction was used to deter large-scale war.

Communication and Information Technology

- Radar was first used to help defend against air attacks on Great Britain. Later it was used to spot German submarines from the air and direct anti-aircraft guns.
- Computer techniques were used in breaking codes.
- Semiconductors were developed and used in navigation systems and later became a key part of computers.

Medicine

- Penicillin began to be widely used to treat infections and other diseases.
- DDT was developed, which killed insects that carried malaria and typhus.

Distribution of U.S. Industry

- Before World War II, much of the industry in the United States was located in the Northeast and Midwest. With the huge increased need for defense industries, manufacturing facilities were built in the South and West.

Use of Resources

- Nearly all luxury or domestic manufacturing ceased during the war, and industries switched to defense manufacturing. For example, automobile plants shifted to making military vehicles.
- Scarce goods such as meat, shoes, sugar, coffee, and gasoline were rationed.

Name _____   Date _____

The War Affects Technology and Industry

Directions: Choose the letter of the *best* answer.

1 Jet planes were first developed for use during World War II by

  A Germany.

  B Great Britain.

  C Japan.

  D the United States.

2 Which development in weaponry changed the world the *most* after World War II?

  A aircraft carriers

  B the atomic bomb

  C jet fighters

  D the submarine

3 How were computer technologies used during World War II?

  A in guiding airplanes

  B in spotting submarines

  C to help soldiers see in the dark

  D in breaking codes

4 Which result was *most likely* caused by the development of DDT during World War II?

  A a lower malaria rate in Central America

  B better nutrition in China

  C a higher literacy rate in Africa

  D better working conditions in the United States

5 How did industry in the United States change during World War II?

  A It became further concentrated in the Northeast.

  B It became focused on manufacturing defense products.

  C Many factories closed down because consumer products were not needed.

  D There was a lack of capital for new factories to be built.

6 How did the United States handle the need for goods such as shoes, sugar, and gasoline during World War II?

  A Domestic production increased.

  B Imports from South America increased.

  C Scarce goods were rationed.

  D New products were developed.

Name _____ Date _____

REVIEW

CALIFORNIA CONTENT
STANDARD 11.7.7

The Atomic Bomb

Specific Objective: Understand the decision to drop atomic bombs and the consequences of the decision.

Read the summary to answer questions on the next page.

The Debate

Reasons To Use the Atomic Bomb	Reasons Not To Use the Atomic Bomb
The invasion of Japan would cost thousands of American lives. Japan might not surrender until it was invaded and conquered. The atomic bomb would end the war and save lives. It was like other weapons in the war, only more powerful. Firebombing of Tokyo and other cities also caused huge casualties. The United States didn't want its investment in developing the bomb to be seen as a waste of time and money. It would show the USSR how powerful the United States was and give the United States more bargaining power after the war.	The Japanese were close to defeat and would have surrendered soon without an all-out invasion. It might have been possible to demonstrate the bomb to the Japanese before dropping it on cities. Some thought Japan would surrender once it saw a demonstration of the bomb's power. Its power was greater than needed to defeat the Japanese. It was a troubling precedent for the United States to be the first in the world to use such a deadly weapon.

The Decision

- Japan was warned that it would face "prompt and utter destruction" if it did not surrender immediately.

- President Truman chose to drop two bombs. He wrote, "The final decision . . . was up to me. . . . I regarded the bomb as a military weapon and never had any doubt that it should be used."

The Immediate Results

- Atomic bombs were dropped on Hiroshima (August 6, 1945) and Nagasaki (August 9).

- About two-thirds of Hiroshima was destroyed immediately; about 66,000 people were killed and 69,000 injured.

- About half of Nagasaki was destroyed immediately; about 39,000 people were killed and 25,000 injured.

- By the end of 1945 about 100,000 more had died from injuries and radiation poisoning.

- Japan agreed to surrender unconditionally about a week after the bombs were dropped.

Name _____   Date _____

CALIFORNIA CONTENT
STANDARD 11.7.7   *The Atomic Bomb*

Directions: Choose the letter of the *best* answer.

1   Why did the U.S. military fear invading Japan in the summer of 1945?

   A   It feared U.S. forces would be defeated if they invaded Japan.

   B   The battles for Iwo Jima and Okinawa showed that an invasion would cost many casualties.

   C   It feared the USSR might be drawn into the war on Japan's side.

   D   There were too many U.S. prisoners of war in Japan who would be endangered during an invasion.

2   Which statement is an argument *for* using the atomic bomb?

   A   Its development had been relatively quick and easy.

   B   It was like other weapons of war, just more powerful.

   C   The USSR had already developed an atomic bomb.

   D   It would be the first bombing attack on the mainland of Japan.

3   Which statement is an argument *against* using the atomic bomb?

   A   Too many people already knew about its existence.

   B   It was too difficult to demonstrate it to the Japanese before using it.

   C   Its power was greater than needed to defeat the Japanese.

   D   The United States could demonstrate its power by being the first to use it.

4   In President Truman's view, the atomic bomb was

   A   a scientific experiment gone astray.

   B   a military weapon that should be used.

   C   an unnecessary and tragic measure.

   D   a matter for the generals to decide.

5   Which statement *best* describes the consequences of dropping atomic bombs on Hiroshima and Nagasaki by the end of 1945?

   A   After the initial impact there were no further casualties.

   B   The only significant consequence reported was eye damage.

   C   There was an outbreak of skin disease but few further casualties.

   D   There were several thousand casualties beyond the initial impact.

Name _____   Date _____

REVIEW

CALIFORNIA CONTENT
STANDARD 11.7.8   *The Marshall Plan*

Specific Objective: Analyze the effect of massive aid given to Western Europe under the Marshall Plan to rebuild itself after the war and the importance of a rebuilt Europe to the U.S. economy.

Read the chart to answer questions on the next page.

The Marshall Plan	Importance of U.S. Economy
After World War II, Western Europe was in chaos. Factories had been destroyed. Millions were living in refugee camps. Poverty and unemployment rates were high. Harsh winter weather in 1946–1947 damaged crops, cut off water transportation, and caused a fuel shortage.	The U.S. economy had grown very large during World War II. After the war, it feared the return of the depression conditions of the 1930s. It needed strong markets for food and manufactured goods.
Secretary of State George Marshall proposed a plan to aid any countries in Europe rebuilding from the destruction of World War II. It required European countries to cooperate to develop a common plan for recovery. The Soviet Union refused to participate.	The Marshall Plan prevented Europe, and therefore the United States, from falling into economic depression. Much of the money from the Marshall Plan was spent on American goods transported in American ships. The Marshall Plan helped the United States maintain a strong economy and world economic leadership.
Under the Marshall Plan, the United States provided $13 billion in aid to 16 countries between 1947 and 1952. The goal was to create stable market-based economies that would promote democratic institutions. By the mid-1950s, most countries of Western Europe were U.S. allies with strong economies. West Germany was brought back into the rebuilt European community.	The plan promoted free trade between Europe and the United States. Europe became a favorable place for American investment. It strengthened capitalism as an economic system against Soviet communism. Communism was less appealing to European voters when democracy resulted in good economic conditions.

Name _____ Date _____

PRACTICE

CALIFORNIA CONTENT
STANDARD 11.7.8

The Marshall Plan

Directions: Choose the letter of the *best* answer.

Use the graph to answer questions 1 and 2.

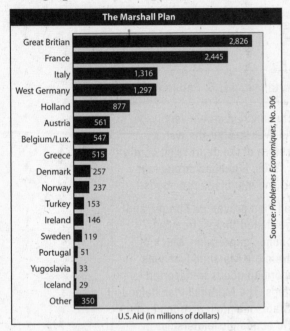

The Marshall Plan

Country	U.S. Aid (in millions of dollars)
Great Britian	2,826
France	2,445
Italy	1,316
West Germany	1,297
Holland	877
Austria	561
Belgium/Lux.	547
Greece	515
Denmark	257
Norway	237
Turkey	153
Ireland	146
Sweden	119
Portugal	51
Yugoslavia	33
Iceland	29
Other	350

U.S. Aid (in millions of dollars)

Source: *Problemes Economiques*, No. 306

1 Based on the graph, what can you conclude about countries that received aid under the Marshall Plan?

A The aid only went to U.S. allies.

B The aid helped Germany rebuild.

C The aid was important for the USSR.

D Only large countries received aid.

2 What can you conclude from the graph about the amount of aid distributed by the Marshall Plan?

A Billions of dollars were distributed in total U.S. aid.

B All countries received less than a billion dollars each.

C Most countries received less than a million dollars each.

D The amount of aid was too small to have an economic impact.

3 How did the Marshall Plan promote unity in Europe after World War II?

A It motivated countries to form a military alliance.

B It required European countries to work together on a plan for economic recovery.

C It united European countries under a common government.

D It established a common currency throughout the countries of Western Europe.

4 How did assistance to Europe after World War II help the U.S. economy?

A It helped the United States to get rid of surplus goods from the war years.

B It raised tariffs to protect U.S. manufacturers from cheap European goods.

C It prevented migration to the United States by unemployed Europeans.

D It provided strong markets for U. S. food and manufactured goods.

5 Which statement *best* describes a political reason for providing aid through the Marshall Plan?

A A strong economy helped liberal candidates get elected in democracies.

B If a country's economy was strong, communism was less attractive to voters.

C Truman hoped to get re-elected, and strong support from Europe would help him.

D Strong economies would allow European countries to join the United Nations.

REVIEW

CALIFORNIA CONTENT
STANDARD 11.8.1

Growth of the
Service Economy

Specific Objective: Trace the growth of service sector, white collar, and professional sector jobs in business and government.

Read the summary to answer questions on the next page.

Changing Types of Jobs

- U.S. technology changed the demand for industrial and manufacturing jobs. Automation (use of machines to perform tasks previously done by people) meant that fewer workers were needed to keep production levels high.

- White-collar jobs (those not using manual labor) increased, while blue-collar jobs (using manual labor of some type) decreased.

- Most blue-collar workers had manufacturing jobs. White-collar workers had higher paying clerical, managerial, or professional jobs in fields like sales, advertising, insurance, and communications.

- Before World War II in 1940, only about 31 percent of jobs were classified as white collar. The percentage grew to 36 percent in 1950 and 47 percent by 1970.

- The government began to employ a much higher percentage of workers as it provided more services to people. The percentage grew from about 13 percent of all workers in 1940 and 1950 to about 18 percent in 1970.

Growth of Corporations

- After the Depression, large companies did not want to rely on a single type of business that could go bankrupt in an economic crisis.

- Large companies bought other types of businesses not necessarily connected to their original work.

- Diversified companies were called conglomerates.

- For example, International Telephone and Telegraph bought car-rental companies, hotel and motel chains, and insurance companies.

- Conglomerates became very powerful and affected how their workers thought and acted as well.

Effect on Culture

- Many employees of large corporations or conglomerates were paid well and had safe, secure, white-collar jobs.

- However, their employers wanted them to put the company first and to conform to certain forms of thought, dress, and social activities.

- A book, *The Organization Man*, showed how corporations supported and increased conformity.

- In the later 1950s and throughout the 1960s, some people questioned whether the economic and social rewards for conformity were worth the loss of some creativity and individuality.

Name _____ Date _____

Growth of the Service Economy

Directions: Choose the letter of the *best* answer.

1 **How did automation change the American workplace after World War II?**

  A It reduced the number of white-collar workers and reduced production.

  B It increased the number of white-collar workers and kept production high.

  C It increased the number of blue-collar workers and increased production.

  D It had little effect on the types of jobs but dramatically increased production.

2 **Which sector of the economy was *most* affected by the changes in the blue-collar workforce after World War II?**

  A government

  B managerial

  C manufacturing

  D professionals

3 **After World War II, the U.S. government**

  A hired more workers as it provided more services to people.

  B was prevented from hiring more people by conservative members of Congress.

  C cut many war-related jobs and decreased the number of government workers.

  D went through several cycles of hiring more and then fewer people.

4 **Which statement *best* describes why large companies became conglomerates after World War II?**

  A They wanted to concentrate on the type of business they knew the best.

  B They thought they could get more political power to influence decisions.

  C They wanted to make their companies less vulnerable to economic crises.

  D They could control tariffs more easily and protect their exports.

5 **White-collar employees of large corporations in the 1950s and 1960s were**

  A expected to be very creative and to try new ways of doing things.

  B not paid well but had good insurance and other benefits.

  C interested in joining labor unions in large numbers.

  D expected to conform to certain ways of thought and dress.

6 **Which description *best* fits the "organization man" of the 1950s?**

  A a worker who increases efficiency through better organization

  B a worker who puts the company first and fits in with the other workers

  C a union leader who organizes a union in a new company

  D the head of a conglomerate who decides on how to organize the company

REVIEW

CALIFORNIA CONTENT STANDARD 11.8.2   *Mexican Immigration*

Specific Objective: Describe the significance of Mexican immigration and its relationship to the agricultural economy, especially in California.

Read the summary to answer questions on the next page.

Braceros

- Since the end of the Civil War, growers depended on migrant workers to pick crops in California and the Southwest.
- During World War II, there was a labor shortage in the United States because so many workers were in the army and in defense industries.
- One area where there was a critical shortage was in low-paying agricultural work.
- The U.S. and Mexican governments started a program to allow Mexicans to come to the United States temporarily to work picking crops and doing other manual labor.
- The Mexican workers were called *braceros* (from the Spanish word for arm, *brazo*), a common term for workers.
- Pay was low, and the governments made all arrangements for food, shelter, transportation, and medical care.
- When their contract for work was done, the braceros were returned to Mexico. However, many stayed in the United States illegally and continued as migrant farm workers. About 4 million people worked through the program until it ended in 1964.
- Farm owners supported the program because it was a source of cheap labor. Those who sought better working conditions for migrant farm workers opposed it. In the context of the civil rights movement of the 1960s the program was finally ended.
- Two Mexican Americans, César Chávez and Dolores Huerta, succeeded in organizing a union in 1962 that became the United Farm Workers of America.

Mexican Immigration

- Beginning in the 1950s, millions of Mexicans began immigrating to the United States. Most immigrated legally. About 4.8 million came in illegally.
- More came to California than any other state. Almost one-third of all Mexican Americans in the United States live in California.
- Today, Hispanic people are the largest minority group in the United States. The 2000 census showed there were about 35.3 million Hispanics (about 60 percent of whom are Mexican Americans), about 12.5 percent of the population.
- California has the largest Hispanic population in the country; more than 30 percent of Californians are Hispanic.
- Most now live in cities, but migrant workers are still important to agriculture in California and other states.

Name _____ Date _____

Mexican Immigration

Directions: Choose the letter of the *best* answer.

1 How did Mexican immigrants affect the growth of agriculture in California?

A Migrant farm workers from Mexico were a critical source of cheap labor.

B Mexican immigrants brought modern farming methods that were taught to California farmers.

C The influx of immigrants made it hard for California to keep its food prices competitive.

D Mexican immigrants had little impact on agriculture.

2 Why was the bracero program created during World War II?

A The United States wanted to strengthen its alliances with its neighbors.

B American farm workers wanted too much money.

C The government wanted to prevent labor unrest during the war.

D The war created a labor shortage all over the United States.

3 The bracero program began as an agreement between

A the U.S. and Mexican governments.

B individual workers and labor agencies in the United States.

C the government of California and the Mexican government.

D growers and workers who were willing to travel to the United States.

4 When their contract for farm work was completed, braceros were intended to

A take jobs in defense industries.

B stay on the farm until the next picking season.

C return to their families in Mexico.

D stay in the United States and become citizens.

5 Why did the United Farm Workers union oppose the bracero program?

A The union wanted to keep minority groups from joining.

B It thought farm owners exploited the braceros as a source of cheap labor.

C The braceros often brought diseases from Mexico that harmed the crops.

D The U.S. government wanted to expand the program to include factory jobs.

6 What is *one* way in which Mexican immigration has affected the population of California?

A A majority of people in California are of Hispanic origin.

B Mexican immigrants have only affected rural areas of the state.

C California has the largest Hispanic population of any state.

D California has made Spanish its official language.

Name _____   Date _____

REVIEW

**CALIFORNIA CONTENT
STANDARD 11.8.3**   *Truman's Labor Policy*

Specific Objective: Examine Truman's labor policy and congressional reaction to it.

Read the sequence diagram to answer questions on the next page.

Economic and Labor Trouble after World War II
• Immediately after the war, government controls on the economy ended. Prices rose quickly while wages stayed the same or dropped. • Unions avoided strikes during the war. After the war in 1946, 4.5 million workers (the most in U.S. history) went on strike for higher wages and better conditions. • Many strikes were successful. New Deal policies supported unions and strengthened them.

Truman's Support for Labor and Opposition to Strikes
• Truman generally supported union rights as defined by Roosevelt's New Deal. • Large strikes by workers in major industries (steel, railroads, coal mines) threatened to paralyze the country. • Truman used threats of federal government action to avoid or end strikes. Workers would be drafted as soldiers and ordered to stay on the job. The government would take control of mines and railroads. Unions gave in to the pressure.

The Taft-Hartley Act
• The 1946 elections created a Republican Congress that opposed current labor strength. • In 1947 the Taft-Hartley Act severely limited union activities and strength. It emphasized the rights of employees not to join a union. • Truman vetoed the Taft-Hartley Act, but Congress passed it over his veto. • Congress rejected Truman's request to repeal it after the 1948 election.

The Korean War
• United States troops became involved in the Korean War in 1950. • The United States was again in a war effort, but the government did not use total controls over the economy and industries as in World War II.

Strikes and National Security
• Workers continued to strike for higher wages and better conditions. • Truman tried to end strikes with threats or federal actions. He said strikes threatened national security and the war effort. • Truman responded to a scheduled steel strike in 1952 by seizing steel mills. • The Supreme Court ruled his actions unconstitutional and said he could have used the Taft-Hartley Act to delay the strike. Truman disliked the act so much he refused to use it.

Name _____ Date _____

PRACTICE

CALIFORNIA CONTENT
STANDARD 11.8.3

Truman's Labor Policy

Directions: Choose the letter of the *best* answer.

1 **Which statement *best* describes the economic situation in the United States right after World War II?**

   A Prices rose, wages rose, and workers avoided striking.

   B Prices rose, wages dropped, and workers went on strike.

   C Prices and wages stayed the same, and workers went on strike.

   D Prices and wages dropped, and workers went on strike.

2 **Which statement *best* describes Truman's general position on labor?**

   A He thought unions were only necessary in small businesses, not in large industries like coal and steel production.

   B He thought unions were too strong and supported laws to limit their power.

   C He supported strong unions as defined by Roosevelt's New Deal policies.

   D He supported most union positions except their right to organize in new industries.

3 **What is *one* way Truman used the military to control strikes?**

   A He sent troops to break up strikes and force union members to work.

   B He prevented union members from joining the military after they had been on strike.

   C He threatened to use soldiers to replace striking workers so they could be fired.

   D He threatened to draft striking workers and then order them as soldiers to keep working.

4 **How did the Taft-Hartley Act reflect Congress's response to Truman's labor policies?**

   A It showed that Congress strongly disagreed with Truman's policies.

   B Congress gave in to Truman's demand for a limitation on union activities.

   C Congress believed that government should not be involved in labor policies.

   D It strengthened union powers, but Congress repealed it in Truman's second term.

5 **How did the economic and labor situation during the Korean War compare to the situation during World War II?**

   A Truman favored more regulation of the economy than Roosevelt had.

   B The government did not use the control over the economy and industry that it did in World War II.

   C During both wars, the government allowed the economy and labor to function on their own.

   D During the Korean War, business and labor leaders worked together to prevent conflicts.

6 **Which statement *best* describes the effect of the Taft-Hartley Act?**

   A It limited union powers and emphasized workers' rights not to join a union.

   B It reinforced union rights that had been established during the New Deal.

   C It established the right of military personnel to organize unions.

   D It strengthened union powers but was repealed in Truman's second term.

Name _____   Date _____

REVIEW

CALIFORNIA CONTENT
STANDARD 11.8.4

Postwar Changes in Government Spending

Specific Objective: Analyze new federal spending on defense, welfare, interest on the national debt, and federal and state spending on education, including the California Master Plan.

Read the summary to answer questions on the next page.

Eisenhower, the New Frontier, and the Great Society

- From about 1950 to 1980, government programs took responsibility for improving people's lives in many ways.
- President Dwight Eisenhower (1952–1960) helped enact programs to raise the minimum wage, extend Social Security and unemployment benefits, support public housing, and build interstate highways. He also created a Department of Health, Education, and Welfare.
- President John F. Kennedy's "New Frontier" (1960–1963) was an ambitious plan to expand social programs for health care and education and improve urban areas. The program did not get support from Congress. Kennedy did increase spending for the space program and defense as well as for foreign aid.
- President Lyndon Johnson's "Great Society" (1963–1968) was the greatest expansion of federal involvement in social welfare in U.S. history. Programs included the "War on Poverty," national health care for the elderly and the poor, support for public and private housing, and aid for public and private schools.

Increases in Government Spending

Defense	Social Welfare	Education
• The Cold War spurred defense spending. • The percentage for defense in national budget rose from about 18 percent in 1940 to 32 percent in 1950 and 52 percent in 1960. • The desire to match Soviet space achievements involved billions in spending. Much went to private companies.	• Social Security and unemployment benefits continued. • The "War on Poverty" included public jobs programs for adults and youth. • Medicare and Medicaid provided health care for the elderly and the poor. • Support was provided for low-income housing and for poor urban areas.	• Education acts in the 1960s were among the first to provide federal aid for education. • The California Master Plan begun in 1960 made the state the national leader in higher education. It established three levels of colleges and universities to provide public higher education to all residents.

PRACTICE

CALIFORNIA CONTENT
STANDARD 11.8.4

Postwar Changes in Government Spending

Directions: Choose the letter of the *best* answer.

1 Which president expanded the role of the federal government in social welfare programs the *most*?

   A Eisenhower

   B Johnson

   C Kennedy

   D Reagan

2 The "New Frontier" is associated with

   A increased spending on defense and the space program.

   B establishing Social Security benefits for the elderly.

   C cutting taxes and spending on social welfare programs.

   D the creation of the Department of Health, Education, and Welfare.

3 Medicare and Medicaid were intended to provide

   A money for medical research.

   B a health care plan for government workers.

   C funding for doctors in poorer countries.

   D health care for the elderly and the poor.

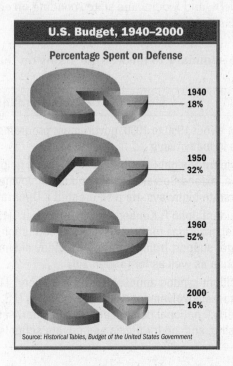

U.S. Budget, 1940–2000

Percentage Spent on Defense

1940 — 18%

1950 — 32%

1960 — 52%

2000 — 16%

Source: *Historical Tables, Budget of the United States Government*

4 According to the chart, the period when defense spending was the greatest percentage of the U.S. budget was

   A just before World War II.

   B just after World War II.

   C during the Cold War.

   D after the Vietnam War.

5 The California Master Plan of 1960 established

   A a system of bilingual education for all children who need it.

   B state support for public and private elementary schools.

   C state achievement standards for high school students.

   D a state system of public college education for residents.

Name _____ Date _____

Expanded Presidential Power

Specific Objective: Describe the increased powers of the presidency in response to the Great Depression, World War II, and the Cold War.

Read the chart to answer questions on the next page.

Expanded Presidential Power		
Great Depression	**World War II**	**Cold War**
• Hoover tried to allow the economy and social problems to improve on their own, but they only got worse. • Roosevelt's New Deal took control of the economy as if it were wartime. The crisis was so severe that the public wanted the government to take strong action. • Programs such as WPA, PWA, and CCC provided jobs for public work paid for by the government. • The Supreme Court opposed some of Roosevelt's programs. The president proposed adding new justices, but was eventually able to find replacements sympathetic to the New Deal. • The federal government made rules for business, including production amounts, workers' pay and hours, and prices. • The government controlled farm production. • Social Security established a retirement program, unemployment benefits, and aid for needy families.	• Even before the United States entered the war, Roosevelt used his power to provide aid to the allies. He met with Churchill to discuss strategy. • Requirements of fighting the war caused government to take control of many businesses. • The War Production Board decided which industries would shift to defense production. • The government controlled prices, wages, and rent; most were frozen to prevent increases (inflation). • Many goods were rationed by government; e.g., people could only buy certain amounts of gas, sugar, coffee, meat each week • Certain labor rights were guaranteed while others were limited. The government had the right to take over certain industries if there was a strike.	• Worldwide competition between the United States and USSR was used by presidents to justify the use of military force around the world without declarations of war. (The U.S. Constitution reserves the right to declare war for Congress.) • To support anticommunist forces around the world, Eisenhower and later presidents used secret military and other actions through the Central Intelligence Agency (CIA). • Presidents used their power to persuade Congress to follow their agendas rather than the president simply responding to laws passed by Congress. • The president and the executive branch became the focus in establishing most foreign and domestic policy.

Name _____   Date _____

PRACTICE

Expanded Presidential Power

Directions: Choose the letter of the *best* answer.

1 Presidential power expanded during the Great Depression because

A Congress refused to take action.

B the economic and social problems were so severe.

C voters passed an amendment to increase the power of the president.

D the threats from foreign countries required immediate action.

2 President Franklin Roosevelt increased the power of the presidency by

A taking over the power to control the tax rate.

B limiting the number of terms a member of Congress could serve.

C taking over the function of many government agencies.

D involving the government in the economy through new agencies and programs.

3 How did the power of the presidency increase during World War II?

A The president expanded the government's role in controlling the economy.

B The president declared war against Japan without congressional approval.

C The president limited the types of cases the Supreme Court could decide on.

D The president prevented Congress from spending too much money.

THAT COMPASS DOESN'T POINT THE WAY I WANT TO GO. CHANGE IT. NOW!

4 The cartoon refers to Roosevelt's *attempt* to increase his presidential power by

A appointing himself Chief Justice of the Supreme Court.

B increasing the number of judges on the Supreme Court.

C reducing the number of representatives in Congress.

D forcing Congress to establish new agencies.

5 The *greatest* changes in presidential power during the Cold War involved

A regulating labor conditions and prices.

B establishing social welfare programs.

C the power to move jobs overseas.

D use of troops without declaring war.

Name _____ Date _____

REVIEW

CALIFORNIA CONTENT
STANDARD 11.8.6

*Environmental Regions
of North America*

Specific Objective: Understand the diverse environmental regions in North America, their relationship to local economies, and the origins and prospect of environmental problems in those regions.

Read the map and summaries to answer the questions on the next page.

Northeast
- Densely populated
- History of industrial production
- Acid rain damage from coal-burning power plants and auto pollution
- Air pollution ("smog") from heavy concentration of autos

South
- Heavily populated urban areas among sparsely populated rural areas
- History of agriculture, textile and paper mills, and chemical plants
- Soil pollution from use of fertilizers and pesticides in agriculture
- Air pollution in urban areas
- Florida and other coastal development includes building in sensitive areas

U.S. Environmental Regions

NORTH CENTRAL

NORTHEAST

WEST

SOUTH

0 _____ 500 Miles
0 _____ 1,000 Kilometers

N

North Central
- Heavily populated urban areas among sparsely populated rural areas
- History of agriculture and heavy industry (This region and the Northeast are referred to as the Rustbelt because of aging factories and power plants.)
- Industry and power production facilities depend on coal, which produces acid rain and smog.
- Soil pollution from use of fertilizers and pesticides in agriculture.

West
- Heavily populated urban areas among very sparsely populated areas; rapid increase in population
- History of ranching, agriculture, mining, and oil production
- Water usage important; most of the area is arid, but water is needed for population growth and industrial development
- Soil pollution from use of fertilizers and pesticides in agriculture
- Conflicts over timber resources and protection of old forests
- Air pollution (smog) from heavy concentration of autos, especially in southern California

National and International Issues
- Acid rain affects many areas; pollutants are created in North Central, Northeast, and South regions and cause severe effects across those regions.
- Nuclear waste from power plants is an unsolved problem. Plants across the country do not have a national storage plan. Wastes do not decompose and cannot be destroyed.

Name _____   Date _____

PRACTICE

Environmental Regions of North America

Directions: Choose the letter of the *best* answer.

1 Which regions are affected the *most* by acid rain?

   A North Central, Northeast, and South

   B North Central, Northeast, and West

   C North Central, South, and West

   D Northeast, South, and West

2 How is air quality affected by the population pattern in the Northeast?

   A The dense population uses advanced technology to produce cleaner air.

   B The dense population results in many autos and problems with smog.

   C Sparse population in rural areas offsets air pollution from urban areas.

   D The population is sparse and public transportation prevents smog problems.

3 What is the *main* cause of soil pollution in the North Central, South, and West regions?

   A acid rain from factories

   B fertilizers and pesticides used in agriculture

   C smog from too many automobiles

   D waste from nuclear power plants

4 The North Central and Northeast regions are sometimes called the Rustbelt because

   A many of their factories and power plants are aging.

   B acid rain makes everything rust there.

   C they are the center of the automobile industry.

   D the steel and iron industry are centered there.

5 In which region of the United States is the issue of water pollution and scarcity the *most* critical?

   A North Central

   B Northeast

   C South

   D West

6 Nuclear waste from power plants is a national issue because

   A facilities to remove the radioactivity are being built across the country.

   B the plants are mostly in the West but wastes are shipped to the Northeast.

   C the plants have all been shut down and Congress regulates them.

   D it does not decompose and there is no national plan for storage.

REVIEW

CALIFORNIA CONTENT STANDARD 11.8.7

Advances in Technology

Specific Objective: Describe the effects on society and the economy of technological developments since 1945, including the computer revolution, changes in communication, advances in medicine, and improvements in agricultural technology.

Read the diagram to answer questions on the next page.

Communication

- Television first became popular in 1950s and increased the spread of a common culture. Now about 99 percent of all households in the United States have a TV. People spend an average of almost 4 hours each day watching it.
- Satellites and other advances bring world events into U.S. homes as the events occur.
- Portable and cellular phones allow people to communicate from almost any location around the world.
- The Internet was first designed for use by the military. It combines computer and communication technology and allows communication by text, audio, and video images. It allows access to worldwide sources of information.

Medicine

- Advances in diagnosis and treatment allow people to live longer than ever; e.g., U.S. life expectancy in 1950 was about 58 years, while in 2000 it was almost 77 years.
- The use of new technology improves eyesight, new products help regulate the heart, and better artificial limbs give greater mobility and function
- New diagnosis tools (MRI, ultrasound) help in the early treatment of many diseases and disabilities.
- New drugs are being used for a variety of physical and mental illnesses, allowing improved quality of life.

Effects of New Technology

Computers

- Computers have become smaller, more powerful, and less expensive.
- Computer technology is now used in nearly every area of life: banking and finance, manufacturing, the medical field, transportation, entertainment, communication, the military, government and elections, appliances, education, science and research
- At the beginning of the 21st century, it was estimated there were about six computers for every ten people in the United States.

Agriculture

- New strains of crops make them more resistant to drought and insects. They can be grown in areas previously not suited or can increase yields per acre. Some people have concerns about genetically modified crops.
- There has been a huge increase in yields during the years since World War II; world food supply can now be almost guaranteed, although distribution is still uneven. Many people in the United States and around the world are hungry and poorly nourished.

Name _____ Date _____

Directions: Choose the letter of the *best* answer.

1 Which statement *best* describes computer technology today?

  A Computers improved rapidly at first, but changes have now slowed down.

  B Everyone in the United States currently owns a computer.

  C Computer technology is involved in nearly every area of our lives.

  D Computers now are smaller, faster, and more expensive than early ones.

2 How has satellite technology changed television since it began in the 1950s?

  A Satellites have increased the cost of television sets dramatically.

  B Satellites have brought worldwide events into American homes.

  C Satellites have decreased the number of news broadcasts on TV.

  D Satellites have increased the number of television stations.

3 How have cellular phones changed the way people communicate?

  A They allow people to communicate easily from almost anywhere.

  B They prevent businesses from using the phone for sales.

  C They limit the number of individuals who can afford phone service.

  D They have become less popular with the increase in e-mail.

4 The Internet was *first* designed for use by

  A businesses.

  B medical researchers.

  C the military.

  D students.

5 Since 1950, life expectancy in the United States has

  A remained about the same.

  B increased slightly, by about 5 years.

  C increased greatly, by about 20 years.

  D dropped slightly because of diseases like cancer and AIDS.

6 Which statement *best* describes changes in agriculture since World War II?

  A Crop yields have gone up; new strains of crops are more resistant to disease and drought.

  B Crops have stayed about the same, but farms are bigger and more efficient.

  C The government has used technology to support the return of families to farming.

  D Better agricultural distribution leaves few people hungry in today's world.

Name _____ Date _____

**CALIFORNIA CONTENT
STANDARD 11.8.8**

Popular Culture After World War II

Specific Objective: Understand forms of popular culture, with emphasis on their origins and geographic diffusion.

Read the summary to answer questions on the next page.

The Spread of Popular Culture

Music

- Jazz originated among African Americans in the South and moved north. Centers of different styles of jazz were New Orleans, Chicago, New York, Kansas City, and the West Coast. Jazz musicians such as Miles Davis, Charlie Parker, and Thelonius Monk were also composers and used improvisation in their music.

- Electronic instruments combined with traditional blues to create rhythm and blues. Alan Freed was a Cleveland, Ohio, disc jockey who first began to play this music in 1951. Rhythm and blues combined with country and pop to produce a new form of music that Freed called rock 'n' roll.

- African-American performers from the South such as Chuck Berry and Little Richard became very popular. Elvis Presley and other white performers began recording this music and brought it to a wider audience.

Professional Sports

- Sports leagues were first integrated after World War II
- Sports became more popular as TV broadcast games across the country

Architecture

- Postwar housing shortages led to mass-produced houses and the growth of standardized suburbs, such as Levittown on Long Island in New York. Similar developments spread throughout the country.

- TV after World War II showed white families in suburbs. It established and spread stereotypes with images of idealized suburban life.

- The growth of suburbs required growth in automobile ownership. This led to a culture created around automobiles, such as motels, drive-in restaurants, drive-in movies, and shopping centers.

Art and Literature

- "Pop art" by Andy Warhol and others in the 1960s took images from advertisements and popular culture—soup cans, comic strips, road signs, and movie posters.

- Science fiction became popular during the 1950s and 1960s when people had fears about nuclear destruction and the growing power of computers.

- Beat culture was centered in San Francisco, Los Angeles, and New York's Greenwich Village in the 1950s. Poets and writers rebelled against social conformity. Their ideas attracted many college students.

Name _____ Date _____

Directions: Choose the letter of the *best* answer.

1 **Why did both jazz and rock 'n' roll have their roots in the American South?**

  A because the music industry was centered there

  B because they were both connected with country music

  C because they were both grounded in African-American culture

  D because the most prominent music schools were located there

2 **Which statement *best* describes the diffusion of beat literature in the 1950s?**

  A It started in New Orleans and spread to northern cities.

  B It started in the South and spread through network television.

  C It started on both coasts and spread to college students.

  D It started in Cleveland and spread through national radio.

3 ***Most* programs on 1950s television reflected images of**

  A rural families working on small farms.

  B single women with careers in business.

  C African-American families living in cities.

  D white families living in the suburbs.

4 **How did architecture reflect the values of the 1950s?**

  A Buildings reflected a burst of creativity after the limitations of the war years.

  B Regional building styles reflected a return to small-town values.

  C New building styles reflected the rebellious spirit of beat culture in cities.

  D Mass-produced houses in the suburbs reflected the culture of conformity.

5 **"Pop art" in the 1960s took images from**

  A advertisements and comic strips.

  B the Korean and Vietnam Wars.

  C photographs of the natural world.

  D the daily lives of working people.

6 **How did professional sports change after World War II?**

  A African Americans were barred from professional teams.

  B Interest in professional sports was spread through nationwide television.

  C Professional sports were limited to elite audiences in big cities.

  D People were more interested in playing sports than watching professional teams.

Name _____ Date _____

REVIEW

CALIFORNIA CONTENT
STANDARD 11.9.1

Shaping Modern Europe

Specific Objective: Understand the establishment of the United Nations and International Declaration of Human Rights, International Monetary Fund, World Bank, and General Agreement on Tariffs and Trade (GATT), and their importance in shaping modern Europe and maintaining peace and order.

Read the diagram to answer the questions on the next page.

Shaping Modern Europe

United Nations and Universal Declaration of Human Rights

- The UN began in April, 1945, with 50 nations. Its mission is to promote peace, improve relations between countries, allow cooperation to solve world problems, and insure human rights. The UN is open to all nations willing to follow its rules.

- All European countries joined the UN after World War II. It provided a forum for debate on issues. Today, nearly every country in the world is a member of the UN.

- The United States and the USSR competed in the UN and around the world in the Cold War. This competition limited the effectiveness of the UN in some cases.

- The UN adopted the Universal Declaration of Human Rights in 1948. It outlined rights to basic freedoms such as those in the U.S. Bill of Rights. It affected the writing of some new constitutions in Europe after the war.

International Monetary Fund (IMF) and the World Bank

- The International Monetary Fund (IMF) was established in 1944 before the end of World War II and began operations in 1947. It was intended to promote international monetary cooperation by allowing money from different countries to be exchanged at fair rates.

- The World Bank was established at the same time to assist reconstruction and development.

- Both function as specialized UN agencies.

- After the war, the World Bank provided loans mostly to European countries to rebuild industries destroyed or damaged by war. These loans strengthened the countries' economies and their ties to the United States.

- Today, nearly every country in the world is a member. Rich, developed nations have the most power in the bank.

General Agreement on Tariffs and Trade (GATT)

- 23 non-Communist countries, including the United States, signed GATT in 1947.

- It was intended to ease barriers to international trade.

- Any tariffs were applied equally to member nations.

- It helped enhance trade within Europe and with the United States. It established strong economic ties among member countries.

- GATT was used until 1995 when the World Trade Organization took over its functions.

Name _____ Date _____

Shaping Modern Europe

Directions: Choose the letter of the *best* answer.

1 The United Nations is open to all nations

  A willing to follow its rules.

  B with democratic governments.

  C with more than 10 million people.

  D who are not in debt.

2 How did the Cold War affect the United Nations?

  A The United States was successful in keeping Soviet countries from joining the UN.

  B The UN became a forum where the United States and the USSR competed for power.

  C The USSR boycotted the UN because its headquarters were located in the United States.

  D Neither the United States nor the USSR were allowed to join the UN because of their Cold War policies.

3 How did the Universal Declaration of Human Rights in 1948 affect Europe?

  A Many nations refused to sign it and refused to join the UN.

  B Civil wars overthrew some dictatorships after the UN passed it.

  C Some new constitutions in Europe reflected its guaranteed rights.

  D The nations that didn't accept it were soon under Soviet control.

4 The International Monetary Fund (IMF) was established to

  A offer loans to democracies in Europe.

  B fund military operations for forces fighting against communism.

  C counter communist economic practices in Soviet controlled areas.

  D encourage nations to cooperate on monetary issues such as exchange rates.

5 How did the World Bank affect relationships between Europe and the United States?

  A It was the only organization that had communist countries and the United States as members.

  B It strengthened ties between Europe and the United States by helping build strong economies.

  C It made the European Union too strong and threatened the United States economy.

  D Europeans did not want to accept loans that would make them indebted to the United States.

6 The General Agreement on Tariffs and Trade (GATT) helped

  A the United States and European countries establish stronger ties through increased trade.

  B the United States force the USSR to trade fairly with satellite nations.

  C South American countries recover from the lack of trade during World War II.

  D Europe and the United States reduce excessive trade during the Cold War.

REVIEW

CALIFORNIA CONTENT
STANDARD 11.9.2

Military Alliances During the Cold War

Specific Objective: Understand the role of military alliances, including NATO and SEATO, in deterring communist aggression and maintaining security during the Cold War.

Read the summary to answer the questions on the next page.

Military Threats during the Cold War

- The USSR was dedicated to expanding communism to other countries around the world after World War II.
- It supported communists in civil wars or internal conflicts in other countries.
- Countries in Eastern Europe were dominated by the USSR, which stationed troops and stockpiled weapons in countries bordering the democracies of Western Europe.
- The USSR attempted to take over West Berlin with a blockade in 1948. Western Europe became more concerned about Soviet aggression.

North Atlantic Treaty Organization (NATO)

- Established in 1949 as a military alliance for mutual protection; included ten European countries, Canada, and the United States
- First military alliance by United States during peacetime in its history
- Greece and Turkey joined in 1952, West Germany in 1955, and Spain in 1980.
- Used for containment of communism in Europe
- NATO and the United States did not provide military support for revolutions against communism in Eastern European countries during 1950s
- Combined forces of 500,000 in Europe by 1952 as well as planes, tanks, and weapons
- In response, Eastern European nations formed the Warsaw Pact in 1955 when West Germany was allowed to re-arm. It provided for mutual defense by any member under attack.
- NATO is still strong today and includes some formerly communist countries (Hungary, Poland, Czech Republic).

Southeast Asia Treaty Organization (SEATO)

- Established in 1954 as a military alliance to offer protection to democracies in Southeast Asia and the South Pacific. It was intended to prevent the spread of communism through military attacks after French withdrawal from Indochina.
- Involved Australia, France, Great Britain, the United States and other countries
- Different from NATO because members did not pledge military assistance against attack
- SEATO approved United States involvement in Vietnam and some members provided troops, but SEATO itself did not provide troops.
- The alliance was disbanded in 1977.

Name _____ Date _____

Military Alliances During the Cold War

Directions: Choose the letter of the *best* answer.

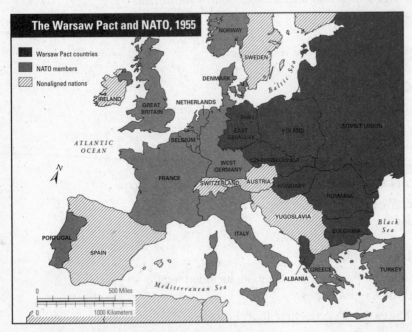

The Warsaw Pact and NATO, 1955

- ■ Warsaw Pact countries
- ■ NATO members
- ▨ Nonaligned nations

NORWAY, SWEDEN, DENMARK, IRELAND, GREAT BRITAIN, NETHERLANDS, BELGIUM, WEST GERMANY, FRANCE, SWITZERLAND, AUSTRIA, HUNGARY, EAST GERMANY, POLAND, SOVIET UNION, CZECHOSLOVAKIA, ROMANIA, YUGOSLAVIA, ITALY, BULGARIA, PORTUGAL, SPAIN, ALBANIA, GREECE, TURKEY, Berlin

ATLANTIC OCEAN, Baltic Sea, Black Sea, Mediterranean Sea

0   500 Miles
0   1000 Kilometers

1 Based on the map, which statement about Europe in 1955 is *true?*

  A All the World War II allies were in NATO.

  B NATO countries had more territory than members of the Warsaw Pact.

  C The Cold War had changed European alliances after World War II.

  D Berlin was located in a NATO country.

2 Which goal *best* describes the USSR's intentions after World War II?

  A to expand communism into countries around the world

  B to convert to a capitalist economy

  C to maintain communism only where it already existed

  D to develop a more democratic form of government

3 Eastern European countries formed the Warsaw Pact in 1955 after

  A France withdrew from NATO.

  B the United States moved nuclear missiles into Turkey.

  C West Germany was allowed to re-arm.

  D Hungarians revolted against the USSR.

4 Why was SEATO formed after France withdrew from Indochina in 1954?

  A to keep European countries from returning to Southeast Asia

  B to keep colonial powers from coming into Southeast Asia

  C to contain the spread of communism in Southeast Asia

  D to form an alliance of Southeast Asia, China, and Japan against the USSR

Name _____ Date _____

The Cold War and Containment of Communism

Specific Objective: Trace the origins and geopolitical consequences of the Cold War and containment policy, including the era of McCarthyism, the Truman Doctrine, the Berlin Blockade, the Korean War, the Bay of Pigs invasion, the Cuban Missile Crisis, atomic weapons testing and policies, the Vietnam War, and Latin American policy.

Read the summary to answer the questions on the next page.

Origins of the Cold War and the Policy of Containment

- The United States and the Soviet Union emerged as dominant after World War II. The Soviets declared that communism and capitalism were incompatible.

- Faced with Soviet aggression, the United States articulated the policy of containment in 1946. Economic and military measures were necessary to prevent the spread of communism to other countries.

- Both superpowers engaged in a nuclear arms race. The United States threatened to use any means, including nuclear weapons, to halt communist aggressors. A doctrine of mutually assured destruction kept both countries on the brink of nuclear war.

Consequences of the Cold War and the Policy of Containment

- The Truman Doctrine (1947) said the United States would provide aid to countries that were trying to resist communism.

- In response to the Berlin Blockade by the Soviets, the United States and Great Britain airlifted supplies into West Berlin and kept the Soviets from taking over the entire city.

- In the Korean War (1951–1953), communist North Korea invaded the democratic South. U.S. and UN troops contained the communist threat.

- The Korean War increased fear of communist activity at home and abroad. Republican Senator Joseph McCarthy made unsupported accusations against members of government. This practice was known as McCarthyism. The lives of many innocent people were ruined.

- In Cuba, communist dictator Fidel Castro received aid from the USSR. In 1961, President Kennedy approved CIA support for an invasion of Cuba at the Bay of Pigs by Cuban exiles. The invasion was a failure and hurt American prestige. In 1962, the Cuban Missile Crisis took the two superpowers to the brink of nuclear war for six days. The crisis was averted when both sides made concessions.

- In 1954, President Eisenhower articulated the domino theory—the belief that if one country in Southeast Asia fell to communism, all would fall. American involvement in the region grew into the Vietnam War. In spite of almost 20 years of guerilla war, the United States was unable to stop the spread of communism. The war sharply divided American opinion.

- Atomic weapons testing in western states such as Nevada harmed the environment. In 1963, the United States and the Soviet Union agreed to a Limited Nuclear Test Ban treaty that barred nuclear testing in the atmosphere.

- The policy of containment also affected Latin American policy. The United States used the CIA to support anticommunist groups in many countries. Many of the U.S.-supported regimes were undemocratic and used brutal tactics to remain in power.

The Cold War and Containment of Communism

Directions: Choose the letter of the *best* answer.

1 **The United States and Great Britain broke the USSR's Berlin Blockade by airlifting supplies into the city. As a result**

   A the United States issued the Truman Doctrine.

   B West Berlin remained free of Soviet control.

   C the Soviets agreed to unite East and West Berlin.

   D the Soviets withdrew completely from German territory.

2 **For the United States, the *main* success of the Korean War was that**

   A the United States formed an alliance with China against the USSR.

   B communism was contained without the use of nuclear weapons.

   C the United States installed a democracy in North Korea.

   D Korea became a united country with a democratic government.

3 **The United States containment policy in Latin America during the Cold War involved using**

   A U.S. troops to fight against communist guerillas.

   B the CIA to support any regime that opposed communism.

   C diplomatic approaches but no military aid or supplies.

   D economic sanctions against countries that turned communist.

"It's Okay—We're Hunting Communists"

COMMITTEE ON UN-AMERICAN ACTIVITIES

HERBLOCK
Oct 47

4 **According to the cartoon, Congressmen investigating suspected communists**

   A did not search hard enough to find communist sympathizers.

   B were usually off-track in their investigations.

   C concentrated their search in cities.

   D were willing to trample the rights of citizens as they hunted communists.

5 **What did the Cuban Missile Crisis reveal about the Cold War?**

   A The Soviet Union confined the spread of communism to Europe.

   B The threat of nuclear war was a constant danger.

   C The United States was much more powerful than the Soviet Union.

   D There were communist spies in the U.S. government.

Name _____   Date _____

CALIFORNIA CONTENT STANDARD 11.9.4

Relationship of Foreign and Domestic Policy

Specific Objective: List the effects of foreign policy on domestic policies and vice versa.

Read the diagram to answer the questions on the next page.

Citizens' Views Shape Foreign Policy

Vietnam War Protests

- Opposition to the war formed quickly after the Gulf of Tonkin Resolution in 1964. The resolution authorized the use of U.S. troops to support South Vietnam against communist North Vietnam. Student organizations began mass protests in 1965.
- African Americans joined protests against the war because of the large percentage of African-American soldiers.
- Protests increased after the Tet offensive in January, 1968. The growing opposition caused President Lyndon Johnson to decide against running for a second term.
- Newly elected President Nixon began pulling out U.S. troops in January, 1969, but engaged in secret bombing attacks against North Vietnam, Laos, and Cambodia.
- Nixon's policies cost him political support. In 1970, news came out that U.S. forces had invaded Cambodia. More than 1.5 million students closed down about 1,200 campuses. Students were killed by National Guard troops at Kent State and Jackson State universities.
- Lack of support at home and lack of success in Vietnam eventually prompted complete withdrawal of U.S. troops in 1973 by President Nixon.
- The war left many Americans with a more cautious attitude toward foreign affairs.

Nuclear Freeze Movement

- Nixon's policy of détente with the Soviet Union led to the SALT I Treaty in 1972. The treaty limited the numbers of certain kinds of nuclear weapons.
- In 1980, the U.S. Senate failed to ratify the SALT II Treaty. President Carter withdrew his support for the treaty because of the Soviet invasion of Afghanistan.
- President Carter then proposed a large buildup of troops and arms. President Reagan increased defense spending even more.
- Groups in the United States in 1980 proposed a freeze on all testing, production, and deployment of nuclear weapons and the aircraft used for them by the United States and the USSR.
- The USSR supported the freeze proposal at the United Nations in 1982 along with many other nations. One million people demonstrated in support in New York City.
- The freeze proposal passed overwhelmingly on state and local ballots in 1982.
- Disagreements arose within the United States and between the United States and the USSR over the types of nuclear arms to limit.
- This movement was an important factor in the treaties several years later that led to limitation of nuclear weapons by about two-thirds.

PRACTICE

CALIFORNIA CONTENT
STANDARD 11.9.4

*Relationship of Foreign
and Domestic Policy*

Directions: Choose the letter of the *best* answer.

1 **Why did opposition to the Vietnam War grow after the Gulf of Tonkin Resolution in 1964?**

  A because U.S. troops started going to Vietnam in large numbers

  B because people wanted the United States to stop bombing Cambodia

  C because there was fear of a nuclear war with China over Vietnam

  D because the United States was spending too much money in Vietnam

2 **One reason many African-American leaders opposed the Vietnam War was that**

  A it helped defense industries that did not hire African Americans.

  B the U.S. Army was still largely segregated.

  C a high percentage of the troops fighting the war were African American.

  D Congressional leaders had not passed enough civil rights legislation.

3 **How did opposition to the war affect President Johnson?**

  A He decided not to run for reelection in 1968.

  B He began to withdraw U.S. troops from Vietnam.

  C He ended the draft in order to regain political support.

  D He ordered a secret invasion of Cambodia to try to end the war.

4 **President Carter withdrew support for the SALT II treaty in 1980 because**

  A he did not have enough support to run for reelection.

  B he did not think it reduced nuclear arms enough.

  C Iran had seized U.S. hostages.

  D the USSR had invaded Afghanistan.

5 **In 1980, the nuclear freeze movement proposed that**

  A the United Nations freeze all funds of nations producing nuclear weapons.

  B the United States and the USSR stop testing, producing, and deploying nuclear weapons.

  C nuclear powers prevent other countries from developing weapons by freezing trade with them.

  D existing nuclear weapons should be stored in a single place where their use could be monitored.

6 **The nuclear freeze movement helped**

  A stop Iran and other countries from developing nuclear capabilities.

  B push the United States toward reductions in nuclear arms through international treaties.

  C prevent the construction of more nuclear power plants across the United States.

  D limit defense spending and increase spending on education and other social services.

REVIEW

CALIFORNIA CONTENT STANDARD 11.9.5   *The End of the Cold War*

Specific Objective: Analyze the role of the Reagan Administration and other factors in the victory of the West in the Cold War.

Read the summary to answer the questions on the next page.

Economic Problems in the USSR

- The communist economy performed poorly over many years. Problems included inefficient industrial production, shortages and poor quality goods, and poor farm output, which resulted in dependence on food imports.
- Heavy investment in the military was required as part of Cold War competition but did not result in economic gains.
- Satellite nations in Eastern Europe controlled by the USSR required military presence. These countries also depended on the USSR for economic support.
- An invasion to retain control of Afghanistan in 1979 began a long war that helped drain the economy.

US Actions in the Cold War

- The United States and the NATO military alliance forced the USSR to continue spending heavily on military goods and troops.
- U.S. support for dissidents in the USSR and Eastern Europe helped provide hope for opponents of communism.
- President Reagan proposed a huge new military buildup beginning in 1981. His program included increases in nuclear weapons and a new missile defense system.

The Fall of Communism in the USSR

- The Soviet economy was near collapse by 1985. The USSR was unable to fund the war in Afghanistan, support satellite nations, and compete with the U.S. military buildup.
- Soviet leader Mikhail Gorbachev began radical economic changes in the USSR in 1985 and began to move toward more openness and free elections.
- Gorbachev realized that better relations with the United States would allow reduction in military spending and economic reform. This resulted in arms-control treaties.
- The changes increased nationalism in non-Russian republics. They declared their independence in 1991 and formed a loose federation. The Cold War officially ended in 1992.

Eastern Europe Breaks with the USSR

- Gorbachev encouraged independence of satellite nations and reduced troops there.
- In 1987, President Reagan encouraged Gorbachev to remove the Berlin Wall.
- East Germany rejected Communist control and tore down the Berlin Wall in 1989. East Germany reunited with West Germany in 1990.
- Other countries established new governments and free elections as well, including Poland, Czechoslovakia, Hungary, Romania, Bulgaria, and the Baltic states.

PRACTICE

CALIFORNIA CONTENT
STANDARD 11.9.5

The End of the Cold War

Directions: Choose the letter of the *best* answer.

1 The communist economy in the USSR before 1979

   A was a world leader in production of consumer goods.

   B used an efficient planning process to control production and prices.

   C had performed very poorly over many years.

   D had many ups and downs just like the capitalist economy in the United States.

2 How did the Cold War affect the economy of the USSR?

   A Investment in new technology helped the economy grow.

   B Competition with the United States spurred the development of new products.

   C Satellite countries contributed to the growth of a thriving economy.

   D The nuclear arms race was a drain on the economy.

3 What effect did the 1979 invasion of Afghanistan have on the USSR?

   A It started a long war that was a factor in economic collapse.

   B It led to a better relationship with the United States.

   C It strengthened the Soviet power in the Middle East.

   D It caused rebellion in Soviet satellite countries.

4 How did Ronald Reagan's actions contribute to the end of the Cold War?

   A He increased U.S. defense spending, which put extra pressure on the Soviet economy.

   B He encouraged satellite nations to rebel against Soviet rule.

   C He engaged in a policy of détente with the Soviets and took the lead in arms-control talks.

   D He encouraged Russian reformers to stage a rebellion against Gorbachev.

5 How did Gorbachev's policies affect Soviet society?

   A His economic reforms made the Soviet Union competitive with the United States.

   B His ideas of openness and reform led to independence for former satellites.

   C He strengthened the military, which led to the final collapse of the economy.

   D He tightened the control of the communist party over all aspects of life in Russia.

6 After the Berlin Wall was opened in 1989, East Germany

   A became an independent republic within the Russian federation.

   B prevented communists from leaving the country.

   C continued as a Communist state but was independent of the USSR.

   D reunited with West Germany.

Name _____ Date _____

REVIEW

CALIFORNIA CONTENT
STANDARD 11.9.6

U.S. Policy in the Middle East

Specific Objective: Describe U.S. Middle East foreign policy and its strategic, political, and economic interests, including those related to the Gulf War.

Read the summary to answer the questions on the next page.

U.S. Foreign Policy and Interests in the Middle East since World War II

- The United States became the dominant power in the region as former European colonies became independent after World War II.

- The United States, along with Great Britain, the USSR, and the UN, supported the establishment of Israel as a Jewish state in 1948. Support for Israel, including weapons and economic aid, has embroiled the United States in conflicts between Israel and its neighbors. The United States has served as a mediator at times with varying degrees of success. The most important agreement was the Camp David Accords in 1978, which led to a treaty between Israel and Egypt.

- President Eisenhower extended the policy of containment and the Truman Doctrine (providing military and economic aid to free nations facing internal or external threat) to the Middle East in 1957. This policy led to conflict with countries such as Egypt, which received aid from the USSR. The United States wanted to keep access to the Suez Canal open because of its strategic location linking the Red Sea and the Mediterranean.

- As in Latin America, the United States sometimes supported corrupt dictators in the region who were friendly to the United States and opposed communism. Support for the shah of Iran led to the Iran hostage crisis in 1979–1980.

- Beginning with President Nixon, the policy of containment led to a more practical approach based on protecting U.S. interests in the region. Foremost among these is U.S. dependence on foreign oil. American oil companies have been involved in the region since the 1930s. The Middle East oil industries were nationalized in the 1960s, and the Organization of Petroleum Exporting Countries (OPEC) was created. OPEC's control of much of the world's oil supply led to oil shortages and price increases during the 1970s.

- To protect its interests, the United States has established military bases in friendly countries such as Saudi Arabia and Qatar throughout the region. Many Arabs, especially Muslim fundamentalists, oppose the U.S. presence and what they see as its unconditional support of Israel.

- Iran and Iraq fought a long war during the 1980s. The United States backed Iraq and Saddam Hussein because of strong opposition by Iran to the United States.

- Saddam Hussein's invasion of Kuwait in 1990 led to the Gulf War in 1991. Iraq's move was seen as a threat to oil fields in Saudi Arabia, and a severe threat to U.S. oil supplies. The United States formed a large international coalition and led troops against Iraq. After a six-week long war, Kuwait was liberated, but Hussein remained in power in Iraq. The United States then asked the UN to impose economic sanctions against Iraq in order to prevent the country from rearming or building nuclear weapons.

- U.S. involvement in the Middle East escalated in response to terrorist attacks in 2001. President George W. Bush's "War on Terror" led to military action against Iraq. U.S. troops invaded in 2003, ousting Saddam Hussein. Then, backed by strong U.S. military presence, Iraq began the slow process of rebuilding.

Name _____ Date _____

U.S. Policy in the Middle East

Directions: Choose the letter of the *best* answer.

1 Which statement *best* describes U.S. policy regarding Israel?

A The United States has remained neutral in disputes between Israel and its neighbors.

B The United States withdrew its support of Israel during the Cold War.

C The United States strongly supports Israel with economic and military aid.

D The United States has failed to negotiate any treaties between Israel and its neighbors.

2 How did the policy of containment relate to the Middle East?

A The United States extended aid to help countries in the region fight communism.

B The United States refused to trade with countries that were run by dictators.

C The United States allied with Muslim fundamentalists to fight communism.

D It had no relevance because the USSR had no interest in the region.

3 What U.S. policy led to the Iran hostage crisis in 1979?

A support for Iraq in its war against Iran

B support for Israel in a conflict with Iran

C support for U.S. oil companies in Iran

D support for its ally, the shah of Iran

4 Why is it important for the United States to have good relations with OPEC?

A It is an important ally in fighting communism.

B It controls access to the Suez Canal.

C It controls the supply and prices of needed oil.

D It is an important ally in supporting Israel.

5 President Nixon's Middle East policy was based on

A a practical approach that focused on protecting U.S. interests.

B a commitment to containing the spread of communism.

C a desire to establish U.S. colonies in the region.

D using economic sanctions against Muslim fundamentalists.

6 Which of its vital interests in the Middle East led the United States into the Gulf War in 1991?

A support for anticommunist leaders

B access to the Suez Canal

C protection of U.S. oil supplies

D security of Israel's borders

Name _____ Date _____

CALIFORNIA CONTENT
STANDARD 11.9.7

*The United States
and Mexico*

Specific Objective: Examine relations between the United States and Mexico in the
20th century, including key economic, political, immigration, and environmental issues.

Read the diagram to answer the questions on the next page.

Economic Issues

- U.S. companies invested in Mexico in the early 1900s and owned many factories, oil refineries, mines, and land. The Mexican government seized some foreign property in the 1930s.

- Discovery of large oil reserves in the 1970s prompted the Mexican government to borrow large amounts. When oil prices dropped, the United States helped Mexico by buying oil at higher prices.

- The North American Free Trade Agreement (NAFTA) took effect in 1994. Its purpose was to lower tariffs and increase trade among Mexico, the United States, and Canada. Some argue that the benefit is mainly to large corporations.

- Many U.S. companies located in Mexico, especially along the border, began to take advantage of low labor costs in the 1990s. Working conditions are often poor and dangerous.

- In 1995, the United States loaned Mexico $20 billion to help Mexico avoid an economic crisis.

Immigration

- The bracero program during World War II brought many Mexicans to the United States to work on farms and in industries. Some stayed illegally.

- A huge increase in immigration from Mexico began in the 1960s.

- Economic crisis in Mexico in the early 1990s spurred more immigration—legal and illegal. About 5,000 immigrants enter the United States illegally each day; about 4,000 are returned to Mexico immediately.

United States and Mexico in the 20th Century

Political Issues

- Most Mexican leaders have maintained good relations with the United States. Mexico depends on the United States in many ways.

- A single party (PRI) controlled Mexico from the early 1920s to 2000.

- Drug smuggling from Mexico has become a larger problem since the 1970s.

Environmental Issues

- Mexico's population grew rapidly from the 1940s to 1970, and cities grew larger. Air pollution and other environmental problems around Mexico City and other cities became severe.

- Assembly plants south of the Texas border built during the 1990s do not follow the same environmental standards as the United States. Heavy pollution from these plants affects U.S. border.

Name _____   Date _____

PRACTICE

CALIFORNIA CONTENT
STANDARD 11.9.7

The United States and Mexico

Directions: Choose the letter of the *best* answer.

1 Which statement *best* describes the U.S. role in the Mexican economy before the 1930s?

  A U.S. businesses built model factories for Mexican workers.

  B U.S. businesses owned a great deal of Mexican land and productive resources.

  C U.S. businesses were forbidden to invest in Mexico by the Mexican government.

  D U.S. businesses considered Mexico a poor place to invest their money.

2 How did the United States respond to the discovery of large oil reserves in Mexico in the 1970s?

  A U.S. oil companies took over most of the Mexican oil industry.

  B It raised tariffs so the Mexicans would not hurt the oil industry in Texas.

  C It refused to buy Mexican oil because it did not meet U.S. standards.

  D It paid higher prices to help the Mexican oil industry through hard times.

3 How did NAFTA change the relationship between Mexico and the United States?

  A It increased the cost of Mexican imports in the United States.

  B It lowered trade barriers between the two countries.

  C It allowed Americans to invest in Mexican companies for the first time.

  D It forced Mexico to import more goods from the United States.

4 *One* reason for the huge increase in Mexican immigration to the United States during the 1990s was

  A an economic crisis in Mexico.

  B relaxed restrictions by the United States.

  C the need for labor in the United States.

  D the end of immigration from Europe.

5 Which statement *best* describes relations between Mexico and the United States since World War II?

  A They have changed from good to bad depending on who was elected president of Mexico.

  B They have generally been poor because the cultures of the two countries are so different.

  C They have generally been good because Mexico depends on the United States in many ways.

  D Mexico and the United States have not worked well together since illegal immigration increased.

6 Assembly plants built in the 1990s along the Mexican border with Texas have created

  A environmental problems in the region.

  B better jobs for American workers.

  C problems with drug smuggling.

  D disputes over the location of the border.

Name _____ Date _____

African Americans Demand Civil Rights

Specific Objective: Understand how demands of African Americans helped produce a stimulus for civil rights, including President Roosevelt's ban on racial discrimination on defense industries in 1941, and how African Americans' service in World War II produced a stimulus for President Truman's decision to end segregation in the armed forces in 1948.

Read the sequence diagram to answer the questions on the next page.

Building to World War II

Defense industries expanded and needed workers (many men in the armed forces). African Americans were not hired or were offered low-paying jobs. U.S. armed forces were segregated and limited African-American opportunities.

↓

Actions by African Americans

African Americans wanted equal access to defense jobs and to military service. A. Philip Randolph was a leader of the first successful African-American union. He organized a march for Washington, D.C., in 1941. The suggested slogan was "We Loyal Colored Americans Demand the Right to Work and Fight for Our Country." About 100,000 were expected for the march in the segregated city.

↓

Roosevelt Responds

Roosevelt met with Randolph to request canceling the march. Randolph refused. Roosevelt persuaded Randolph to cancel the march. In return, the president issued an executive order banning descrimination in hiring for jobs with federal contracts. He also established a committee to enforce the order.

↓

African-American Service during World War II

African Americans still faced discrimination in the armed services and defense jobs, but there was a great improvement from World War I. About 1 million African Americans served in the armed forces in the war. Many were kept in noncombat roles, but some were highly decorated for their service. About 2 million African-American men and women worked in defense industries. African-American news-papers proposed the Double V campaign during the war. V stood for victory against fascism in Europe and for victory in the struggle for equality.

↓

Truman Responds

After the war, African Americans pushed for equal opportunities in the military and jobs. They met with President Truman to make their demands. Truman proposed civil rights measures but Congress rejected them. Truman used an executive order to force desegregation of all armed forces in 1948.

PRACTICE

CALIFORNIA CONTENT
STANDARD 11.10.1

African Americans Demand Civil Rights

Directions: Choose the letter of the *best* answer.

1 How did the U.S. military treat African Americans *before* World War II?

A   It welcomed African-American men but not African-American women.

B   It only allowed African Americans with a college degree to join.

C   It was segregated and limited African-American opportunities.

D   It did not allow African Americans to join.

2 What did A. Philip Randolph do to push for civil rights in 1941?

A   He was the first African American appointed to a cabinet position.

B   He organized a march to demand equal rights for African Americans.

C   He threatened President Roosevelt with court cases over discrimination in jobs.

D   He led African Americans in opposing many New Deal policies.

3 How did President Franklin Roosevelt respond to African American demands for equal rights?

A   He issued an executive order barring discrimination in jobs with federal contracts.

B   He responded to African-American protests by using troops to control them.

C   He helped African Americans organize protests that influenced Congress.

D   He refused to meet with African-American leaders to discuss their demands.

4 Which statement about conditions for African Americans in World War II is *true*?

A   Millions of African Americans served in the military and worked in defense industries.

B   African Americans were prevented from serving in combat.

C   African Americans moved from cities to rural areas.

D   African-American newspapers were prevented from publishing.

5 The Double V campaign referred to

A   victory against fascism and for communism.

B   victory against fascism and for equal rights.

C   victory against Germany and Japan.

D   voting rights in federal and state elections.

6 Truman used an executive order to end segregation in the military after

A   African-American leaders threatened widespread strikes.

B   receiving pressure from Republicans in Congress.

C   Congress defeated his civil rights measures.

D   African Americans held a large protest march.

Name _____ Date _____

Specific Objective: Examine and analyze the key events, policies, and court cases in the evolution of civil rights, including *Dred Scott* v. *Sandford, Plessy* v. *Ferguson, Brown* v. *Board of Education, Regents of the University of California* v. *Bakke,* and California Proposition 209.

Read the summary to answer the questions on the next page.

Rights as Citizens

- Dred Scott was a slave taken by his owner to a free state (Illinois) then back to a slave state (Missouri). He sued for freedom in 1846 (*Dred Scott* v. *Sandford*), claiming he should remain free.

- The U.S. Supreme Court ruled in 1857 that free African Americans could not become citizens of the United States and had no rights to sue in the courts.

- The power of the federal government to prohibit slavery in new territories was limited.

- In 1868, the Fourteenth Amendment gave African Americans the rights of citizens.

Separate but Equal

- After Reconstruction, Southern states passed Jim Crow laws to prevent African Americans from using the same public facilities as whites.

- Homer Plessy tested the law by sitting in a "whites only" railroad car. *Plessy* v. *Ferguson* claimed separate facilities violated the equal protection clause in the Fourteenth Amendment.

- The Supreme Court ruled in 1896 that separate facilities were legal as long as they were equal. The doctrine of "separate but equal" allowed segregation across the South.

- Oliver Brown sued the school board in Topeka, Kansas, because his daughter had to attend a school far away instead of one nearby for whites only.

- Lawsuits from other states challenging "separate but equal" schools were combined into *Brown* v. *Board of Education.*

- The result was a unanimous decision by the Supreme Court in 1954 which ruled that segregated schools were unequal by their very nature of being separate.

- Schools resisted desegregation and further court orders were required.

Affirmative Action

- "Affirmative action" was first used by President Kennedy to describe programs that would favor African Americans in jobs and admission to colleges.

- Opponents claimed the policy discriminated against more qualified whites.

- In *Regents of the University of California* v. *Bakke* (1978), the Supreme Court ruled that a rigid quota system for university medical school admission was unfair. It had allowed race to be one factor considered for entry into the program.

- In 1996, California voters passed California Proposition 209, ending state-controlled affirmative action programs. Minority enrollments in California universities dropped.

Name _____   Date _____

PRACTICE

Civil Rights in the Courts

Directions: Choose the letter of the *best* answer.

1 **The Supreme Court ruling in the case of *Dred Scott* v. *Sandford* in 1857**

  A helped limit the spread of slavery into new territories.

  B gave free African Americans the right to vote.

  C denied the rights of any African Americans to be citizens.

  D prevented owners from selling slaves to people in free states.

2 **The issue in *Plessy* v. *Ferguson* in 1896 was whether African Americans**

  A would be required to pay a poll tax to vote.

  B could sue anyone in federal court.

  C had the right to vote in primary elections.

  D could use the same facilities as whites.

"Our Constitution is color blind, and neither knows nor tolerates classes among citizens."

—Supreme Court Justice Harlan, 1896

---

3 **What does this quotation show about Justice Harlan's views about civil rights?**

  A He supported separate schools for African Americans.

  B He thought it was too soon to give African Americans equal rights.

  C He disagreed with the majority of the Supreme Court.

  D He did not think African Americans could be citizens.

4 **The *Brown* v. *Board of Education* case in 1954 overturned the ruling of**

  A *Dred Scott* v. *Sandford*.

  B *Plessy* v. *Ferguson*.

  C *Regents of the University of California* v. *Bakke*.

  D California Proposition 209.

5 **What did the Supreme Court rule against in *Regents of the University of California* v. *Bakke*?**

  A affirmative action programs that set a rigid quota for minority admissions

  B a medical school that denied admission to qualified African Americans

  C the unfair distribution of financial aid to minority students

  D separate medical schools for whites and African Americans

6 **What was the purpose of California Proposition 209?**

  A to prohibit discrimination in public schools

  B to end affirmative action in state programs

  C to promote equal rights in hiring for state jobs

  D to end segregation in restaurants and buses

Name _____ Date _____

Lawyers Challenge Segregation in Higher Education

Specific Objective: Describe the collaboration on legal strategy between African American and white civil rights lawyers to end racial segregation in higher education.

Read the summary to answer the questions on the next page.

A New Legal Strategy Challenges *Plessy* v. *Ferguson*

- Before 1930 the NAACP relied on volunteer efforts of white lawyers such as Arthur Spingarn to challenge segregation.

- In 1930 it received a grant from a young philanthropist from Harvard and hired Nathan Margold, a Jewish lawyer from New York, to study the lack of funding for black schools. He proposed using the Fourteenth Amendment to challenge inequality in public schools.

- Charles Hamilton Houston, an African-American graduate of Harvard Law School, greatly strengthened the law school at Howard University. He trained a new generation of skilled African-American lawyers, including Thurgood Marshall.

- Houston focused on graduate and professional programs rather than public schools as a way to challenge segregation. Most African Americans in the South had little access to graduate education. This approach would show that there were not really "separate but equal" opportunities for them.

Cases Attack "Separate but Equal" in Higher Education

- In 1936 Houston and Marshall won the case of *Pearson* v. *Murray* that forced the University of Maryland law school to admit a black student.

- Marshall took over leadership of the team in 1938 and became head of the new NAACP Legal Defense Fund in 1939. The strategy was to find the best test cases to bring to the Supreme Court.

- Cases between 1938 and 1950 led to rulings that required professional schools at state-supported universities in Missouri, Oklahoma, and Texas to admit black students and treat them equally. The federal government begn to actively support the NAACP.

Support from Whites

- Franklin Roosevelt and Harry Truman appointed more liberal justices to the Supreme Court who were supportive of the arguments of the NAACP lawyers.

- Most of the leading NAACP lawyers were African Americans. Jack Greenberg was a Jewish lawyer who joined the team in 1949 and argued many important cases.

Brown Decision Ends Segregation in Public Education

- Higher education set the precedent to show that "separate" could not be "equal."

- Combining cases from around the country, the Supreme Court finally ruled in *Brown* v. *Board of Education* (1954) to overturn *Plessy*. The entire basis of segregation and Jim Crow laws was thrown out.

PRACTICE

CALIFORNIA CONTENT
STANDARD 11.10.3

Lawyers Challenge
Segregation in Higher
Education

Directions: Choose the letter of the *best* answer.

1 **Which phrase *best* describes the focus of Charles Houston's legal strategy against segregation?**

A funding for public schools in black neighborhoods

B the First Amendment and freedom of speech

C lack of equal opportunities for professional education

D discrimination in military training

2 **What role did Howard University play in the fight against segregation?**

A It trained African Americans to teach in public schools.

B A philanthropist from Howard helped support NAACP legal battles.

C It was the first state-supported law school forced to accept black students.

D Many NAACP lawyers were trained at Howard Law School.

3 **What was the significance of the Supreme Court's ruling in *Pearson* v. *Murray* in 1936?**

A It was the first victory for Charles Houston's legal strategy.

B White lawyers changed the NAACP's strategy and finally won a case.

C It ended segregation in public schools in the South.

D It was the first case won by the NAACP Legal Defense Fund.

4 **Which statement *best* describes the way black and white lawyers worked to fight segregation after 1930?**

A Blacks defined the strategy but white lawyers argued the cases in court.

B The strategy was mostly defined and carried out by blacks with white support.

C White lawyers were not involved until blacks had won some important cases.

D There was little white support until after the *Brown* decision in 1954.

5 **In legal terms, the *Brown* decision in 1954**

A overturned states' rights to control private education.

B prevented universities from using the same rules as high schools.

C declared that education was not a public right but a privilege.

D declared the basis for segregation and Jim Crows laws illegal.

6 **How did presidents Roosevelt and Truman support the fight against segregation in higher education?**

A They proposed federal laws to integrate colleges.

B They appointed African Americans to their cabinets.

C They appointed liberal justices to the Supreme Court.

D They allowed African-American veterans to attend college.

Name _____ Date _____

African-American Civil Rights Leaders

Specific Objective: Examine the roles of civil rights advocates including the significance of Martin Luther King, Jr.'s "Letter from Birmingham Jail" and "I Have a Dream" speech.

Read the diagram to answer the questions on the next page.

A. Philip Randolph

- Organized first successful African-American labor union in 1925
- Planned march in Washington, D.C., in 1941; Roosevelt banned discrimination in hiring in defense industries to avoid protest
- Helped plan March on Washington in 1963

Martin Luther King Jr.

- Civil rights leader, president of Southern Christian Leadership Conference
- Led Montgomery bus boycott in 1956
- Philosophy of nonviolent resistance
- "Letter from Birmingham Jail" explained the urgency of protesting against brutal and unfair treatment
- Helped organize March on Washington in 1963; 200,000 people marched
- "I Have a Dream" speech at the march expressed his vision of blacks and whites living together in equality and peace

Malcolm X

- Leader within Black Muslims, group that believed separation from whites was better than integration; later separated from this group
- Differed with King on importance of nonviolence; often called for revolution
- *Autobiography of Malcolm X* explained his beliefs and was widely read

Civil Rights Leaders

Thurgood Marshall

- Director of NAACP Legal Defense Fund (1939–1961) and lead lawyer in many cases, including *Brown* v. *Board of Education,* which overturned school segregation
- Appointed federal judge in 1961 and Supreme Court justice in 1967
- Strong defender of civil rights until resignation from Supreme Court in 1991

Rosa Parks

- Active in NAACP and in civil rights work 1930s–1950s
- Refused to move to the back of a bus so a white man could sit down (1955)
- Sparked the 381-day boycott that led to the desegregation of buses in the South

PRACTICE

CALIFORNIA CONTENT
STANDARD 11.10.4

African-American Civil Rights Leaders

Directions: Choose the letter of the *best* answer.

1 **By planning a protest in Washington in 1941, A. Philip Randolph helped**

   A   end discrimination in defense hiring.

   B   get recognition for the first African-American labor union.

   C   get school segregation overturned.

   D   African Americans get leadership positions in the military.

2 **Martin Luther King, Jr. led civil rights protests that**

   A   focused entirely on equal access to jobs and to equal pay.

   B   mostly targeted racial discrimination in Northern cities.

   C   used nonviolence as their central approach.

   D   stressed the importance of the separation of races.

3 **Martin Luther King, Jr. wrote his "Letter from Birmingham Jail" to explain**

   A   why white people should be more involved in protests.

   B   how to be more patient in seeking civil rights.

   C   the use of force if necessary against the police.

   D   the need to protest against unfair treatment.

4 **Malcolm X and the Black Muslims disagreed with Martin Luther King, Jr. over**

   A   the role of women in the civil rights movement.

   B   the philosophy of nonviolent resistance.

   C   the way the NAACP was fighting segregation.

   D   who should run the Congress of Racial Equality.

5 **Thurgood Marshall was extremely successful as**

   A   the leader of the Southern Christian Leadership Conference.

   B   a union leader of African-American workers.

   C   a planner of the March on Washington in 1963.

   D   a lawyer and judge who supported civil rights through the legal system.

6 **The Montgomery bus boycott of 1956 was sparked by the actions of**

   A   James Farmer.

   B   Martin Luther King, Jr.

   C   Malcolm X.

   D   Rosa Parks.

Name _____   Date _____

The Spread of the Civil Rights Movement

Specific Objective: Understand the diffusion of the civil rights movement of African Americans from the churches of the rural South and the urban North, including the resistance to racial desegregation in Little Rock and Birmingham, and how the advances influenced the agendas, strategies, and effectiveness of the quests of the American Indians, Asian Americans, and Hispanic Americans for civil rights and equal opportunities.

Read the summary to answer the questions on the next page.

Civil Rights and African-American Churches

- Since the end of the Civil War, African-American churches had served as community centers. Church leaders were community leaders as well. Martin Luther King, Jr. was a Baptist minister who was chosen to lead the Montgomery bus boycott.

- After the boycott ended, King and other ministers and civil rights leaders formed the Southern Christian Leadership Conference (SCLC). The SCLC used churches as its base to spread protests and demonstrations throughout the South. Opponents of civil rights often targeted churches. Ella Baker of SCLC helped organize the nationwide Student Nonviolent Coordinating Committee (SNCC).

- Members of Northern churches provided moral support and fought discrimination. Many in the North joined Black Muslim and Black Power movements.

Resistance to Desegregation in Little Rock and Birmingham

- The governor of Arkansas decided to resist school desegregation in 1957. He ordered the National Guard to turn away high school students in Little Rock. A federal judge ordered students admitted, and President Eisenhower ordered troops to help them attend. Students were allowed in but were harassed in school by some whites. The governor closed the school at the end of the year.

- In 1963, Birmingham, Alabama, was the most segregated city in the country. Reverend Fred Shuttlesworth urged Martin Luther King, Jr. and the SCLC to use nonviolence to integrate the city. Protests continued for more than a month. Hundreds were jailed, including King and children. Nationwide television showed police attacking protesters with dogs and fire hoses. Protests, economic boycotts, and negative media coverage convinced leaders in Birmingham to accept changes.

Civil Rights Movement Spreads to Other Minorities

- César Chávez and others organized Hispanic farm workers in California and used a nonviolent protest to get better pay and conditions. Several Latino political organizations such as LULAC and La Raza Unida were formed.

- The American Indian Movement (AIM) formed in 1968 and confronted the government over the rights of Native American tribes to control their affairs. Legal victories for Native Americans included restoration of land in several states.

- Japanese Americans pushed for reparations from internment during World War II. Congress provided payments in 1965 and 1990.

PRACTICE

CALIFORNIA CONTENT
STANDARD 11.10.5

The Spread of the Civil Rights Movement

Directions: Choose the letter of the *best* answer.

1 What role did African-American churches in the North and South play in the spread of the civil rights movement?

  A They often opposed civil rights marches because of their potential for violence.

  B They preferred not to get involved in political activities such as protest marches.

  C They were centers for community action and helped organize civil rights protests.

  D They had too few members to make much of an impact in civil rights actions.

2 How did events in Birmingham, Alabama, in 1963 relate to the SCLC?

  A Members of the SCLC used violent tactics to resist the police brutality in the city.

  B Protests and boycotts organized by the SCLC ended segregation in the city.

  C The SCLC was organized to build on the success of the protests in Birmingham.

  D The SCLC had no role in the civil rights movement in Birmingham.

3 The best-known resistance to school desegregation in 1957 occurred in

  A Birmingham, Alabama.

  B Little Rock, Arkansas.

  C Montgomery, Alabama.

  D Oxford, Mississippi.

4 Which of these groups grew out of the SCLC?

  A AIM

  B LULAC

  C NAACP

  D SNCC

5 Legal victories by Native Americans during the 1970s and 1980s gained

  A restoration of native land in several states.

  B their right to vote in presidential elections.

  C a constitutional amendment guaranteeing payment of reparations.

  D special representatives for each tribe in Congress.

6 Which of the following groups was *most* influenced by the ideas of Dr. Martin Luther King, Jr.?

  A members of the American Indian Movement

  B Latinos who started the brown power movement

  C Hispanic farm workers in California

  D victims of Japanese internment

Name _____   Date _____

REVIEW

CALIFORNIA CONTENT
STANDARD 11.10.6   *Laws Support Civil Rights*

Specific Objective: Analyze the passage and effects of civil rights and voting rights legislation and the Twenty-fourth Amendment, with an emphasis on equality of access to education and to the political process.

Read the summary to answer the questions on the next page.

Civil Rights Act of 1964

Passage

Racial tensions and civil rights protests grew during the early 1960s. In June, 1963, President Kennedy used federal troops to force Governor Wallace of Alabama to desegregate the state university. Kennedy demanded that Congress pass a civil rights law. President Johnson pledged to carry on Kennedy's work. He persuaded Southern senators to stop blocking passage and signed the bill in July, 1964.

Effects

• Prohibited discrimination because of race, religion, national origin, and gender

• Gave the federal government power to protect voting rights and speed up school desegregation. The U.S. Attorney General had power to file desegregation lawsuits.

• Banned discrimination in employment and established the Equal Employment Opportunity Commission to enforce fair treatment in employment

• Banned discrimination in public places such as parks, washrooms, restaurants, and theaters

Twenty-Fourth Amendment

Passage

Poll taxes were still required in five Southern states. Poor African Americans could not afford to pay them and were prevented from voting. Approved by Congress in 1962; ratified by the necessary 38 states in January, 1964.

Effects

• Made poll taxes illegal; extended the right to vote to millions of poor people

Voting Rights Act of 1965

Passage

Southern states had passed laws to limit African-American voting rights guaranteed by the Fifteenth Amendment. During the summer of 1964, known as the Freedom Summer, volunteers worked to register African-American voters in Mississippi. The Freedom Summer sparked racial violence and murder in the state. In 1965, Selma, Alabama, became the focus of voting rights work; arrests and violence followed. President Johnson submitted the Voting Rights Act within days of the largest protests in Selma. Congress passed it within a few months.

Effects

• Eliminated literacy tests often used to disqualify African-American voters

• Allowed federal examiners to register voters who had been denied their rights

• Tripled the number of African Americans registered to vote in the South

PRACTICE

CALIFORNIA CONTENT STANDARD 11.10.6

Laws Support Civil Rights

Directions: Choose the letter of the *best* answer.

1 How did the Civil Rights Act of 1964 affect equal access to education?

A It provided funds to improve local schools for African Americans.

B It created programs to help African Americans improve their reading skills.

C It gave the federal government more power to speed up school desegregation.

D This law was concerned with public accommodations and did not affect education.

2 *One* effect of the Civil Rights Act of 1964 was

A the creation of a federal commission to insure fair employment practices.

B an investigation into federal spending on civil rights cases.

C a nationwide study comparing education in different states.

D the repeal of portions of the Fifteenth Amendment on voting rights.

3 The *specific* effect of the Twenty-fourth Amendment on voting was

A ordering federal observation of state elections.

B outlawing literacy tests.

C eliminating residency requirements.

D eliminating poll taxes.

4 Passage of the Voting Rights Act of 1965 came shortly after

A President Kennedy used federal troops at the University of Alabama.

B Martin Luther King, Jr.'s "I Have a Dream" speech.

C the Freedom Summer campaign in Mississippi.

D violent police response to a voting rights campaign in Selma.

5 How did the Voting Rights Act of 1965 affect voter registration?

A It increased the role of the federal government in voter registration.

B It allowed the federal government to disqualify voters from certain states.

C It allowed states to make their own rules concerning federal elections.

D It established stricter rules to make sure voters registered correctly.

6 How did the civil rights movement affect the passage of civil rights laws in the 1960s?

A The movement had little impact on the passage of important legislation.

B The movement created pressure on Congress and helped pass civil rights laws.

C The movement was effective in getting Southern states to change and made new laws unnecessary.

D The movement created a backlash, and the Supreme Court ruled that the new laws were unconstitutional.

Name _____   Date _____

Women's Rights and Women's Roles

Specific Objective: Analyze the women's rights movement from the era of Elizabeth Stanton and Susan Anthony and the passage of the Nineteenth Amendment to the movement launched in the 1960s, including differing perspectives on the roles of women.

Read the sequence diagram to answer the questions on the next page.

Early Work toward Suffrage and Women's Rights

The 1848 Seneca Falls Convention of 300 women activists stated grievances, the need for equal rights, and women's right to vote. Elizabeth Stanton was one of the organizers. Women were strongly involved in abolition, temperance, and progressive movements.

↓

Nineteenth Amendment

Stanton, Susan Anthony, and others established a national group in 1890 to work for suffrage. Protests before World War I gained suffrage in some states. Women working in industrial and other settings during World War I helped spur passage of the Nineteenth Amendment granting woman suffrage in 1920.

↓

World Wars Bring Changes

Women were needed to work in new roles during wars, such as manufacturing, business, and the military. Fashions and social roles changed. Women were not limited to the roles of homemaker and mother.

↓

Women's Liberation Movement 1960s to 1970s

During the 1950s, more women worked outside the home but were limited to certain jobs. Women's involvement in political activism of the 1960s led to the women's liberation movement. The Presidential Commission on the Status of Women, established in 1961, found that women were paid less than men. The Civil Rights Act of 1964 banned discrimination based on gender. Groups such as the National Organization for Women (NOW) pushed for legal and social changes, such as equal rights in work and education and the right to choose an abortion. The Equal Rights Amendment (ERA) was proposed to guarantee equal rights for men and women. Thirty-five states passed the amendment, three short of the amount needed. The time limit ended in 1982, and the ERA was defeated. Opponents of ERA and the women's liberation movement believed that women should remain in more traditional roles. They were concerned that changes threatened traditional American society.

PRACTICE

CALIFORNIA CONTENT
STANDARD 11.10.7

Women's Rights and
Women's Roles

Directions: Choose the letter of the best answer.

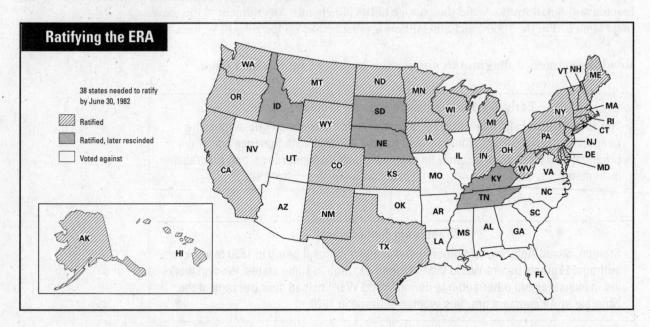

Ratifying the ERA

38 states needed to ratify
by June 30, 1982

▨ Ratified

▩ Ratified, later rescinded

☐ Voted against

---

1 **Based on the map, which region *most* strongly supported the ERA?**

A Northeast

B Northwest

C Southeast

D Southwest

2 **Some people who opposed the ERA suggested that**

A women should be given more rights than the amendment proposed.

B women's liberation was a problem that state governments should handle.

C women's liberation was a threat to traditional American life.

D the amendment should apply to girls as well as adult women.

3 ***One* big change in women's roles during the World Wars was the**

A use of labor-saving appliances at home, such as washing machines.

B number of divorces based on a new federal law passed in the 1920s.

C widespread use of daycare facilities to help raise children.

D number of women who worked in jobs previously reserved for men.

4 **What was *one* of the main findings of the Presidential Commission on the Status of Women in the 1960s?**

A Most suburban housewives were happy with their lives.

B Women were generally paid far less than men.

C Few women were interested in working in nontraditional jobs.

D More women attended college than men did.

REVIEW

**CALIFORNIA CONTENT
STANDARD 11.11.1**

Immigration in the 20th Century

Specific Objective: Understand the reasons for the nation's changing immigration policy, with emphasis on how the Immigration Act of 1965 and successor acts have transformed American society.

Read the chart to answer the questions on the next page.

Policy	Reasons and Results
Immigration before 1965 • 1920s acts restricted immigrants from southern and eastern Europe; virtually no Asians were accepted • Some easing in 1952	• Government believed some immigrants "fit in" to the culture better; some bias against darker-skinned peoples, Jews • More people wanted to immigrate after World War II; more Asian immigrants
Immigration and Nationality Act of 1965 • Quotas for national origin replaced with quotas by hemisphere; amended in 1978 to allow a world total of 270,000 per year, maximum of 20,000 per country • Special status for refugees (1978) • Favored immigrants with certain job skills	• "Great Society" opened the door to non-European immigrants. Tried to correct injustice from earlier limits. Saw a huge increase from Asia and Latin America, most living in California and the Southwest • Many refugees from Latin America • United States was looking for immigrants to fill certain needed jobs
Immigration Reform and Control Act of 1986 • Penalties for employers hiring undocumented immigrants; exceptions for long-term residents	• A huge number of undocumented immigrants were entering the country, especially on the southern border from Mexico.
Immigration Act of 1990 • Increased the total number of yearly immigrants allowed to 675,000 • More immigrants allowed with certain job skills • Tried to increase diversity of origin	• Increased flexibility in the policy • About two-thirds of immigrants were family members of U.S. residents • Increased job-related immigrants, favored skilled workers over unskilled
Illegal Immigrant Reform and Immigrant Responsibility Act (1996) • Made it easier to deport immigrants • Established income test and limited government assistance to immigrants	• The number of undocumented immigrants was large and conflicts arose over their rights and assistance given to them. Some courts are trying to resolve these issues.

Changes in American Population

• 45 percent of immigrants since 1965 are from the Western Hemisphere, primarily Mexico. Hispanic Americans are now the largest minority group in the United States.

• 30 percent of immigrants since the 1960s are from Asia.

• More than half of California residents are members of a minority group.

Immigration in the 20th Century

Directions: Choose the letter of the *best* answer.

1 Before 1965, U.S. immigration policy was

  A biased toward people who were thought to fit in with American society.

  B controlled by the president rather than Congress.

  C more important during the World Wars than at any other time.

  D open to people of all countries, as long as they could prove their job skills.

2 What was *one* reason behind changes in U.S. immigration policy in 1965?

  A a growing need for unskilled factory workers

  B strong sentiment to limit immigration from certain countries

  C a desire to correct problems in the previous system

  D a desire for population growth during the Cold War

3 As a result of the Immigration and Nationality Act of 1965, most immigrants came from

  A Africa and the Middle East.

  B Asia and Africa.

  C Asia and Latin America.

  D Eastern and Western Europe.

4 The United States has responded to the growing numbers of refugees in the world by

  A reducing the number of refugees allowed into the country.

  B allowing refugees to enter from certain countries but not others.

  C requiring refugees to have certain job skills to be accepted.

  D accepting more refugees and giving them special status.

5 The huge number of undocumented immigrants entering the United States has resulted in

  A taxing them to help pay for immigration costs.

  B new programs designed to give them job training and education.

  C greater support for classes in citizenship training.

  D laws that make it harder for them to get jobs and to remain in the country.

6 Immigration since 1965 has contributed to the fact that

  A the majority of California residents are members of a minority group.

  B the number of Hispanic immigrants has decreased.

  C Asian Americans are the largest minority group in the United States.

  D the number of U.S. citizens has decreased.

Name _____ Date _____

Domestic Policy Since World War II

Specific Objective: Analyze the significant domestic policy speeches of Truman, Eisenhower, Kennedy, Johnson, Nixon, Carter, Reagan, Bush, and Clinton.

Read the summary to answer the questions on the next page.

Truman and Civil Rights: "I am asking for equality of opportunity for all human beings . . . and if that ends up in my failure to be reelected, that failure will be in a good cause." Congress did not pass civil rights laws, but Truman ordered the military desegregated.

Eisenhower and School Desegregation: "There must be respect for the Constitution . . . or we shall have chaos." Eisenhower used federal troops to force the governor of Arkansas to allow African Americans to attend a white high school in Little Rock as ordered by the Supreme Court. The troops helped to keep order in the city.

Kennedy and the New Frontier: "We stand on the edge of a New Frontier," which has " . . . uncharted areas of science and space . . . unconquered pockets of ignorance and prejudice, unanswered questions of poverty and surplus." Kennedy proposed ambitious programs for space exploration and social welfare.

Johnson and the "Great Society": "The Great Society is a place where every child can find knowledge to enrich his mind and to enlarge his talents, . . . where . . . man serves not only the needs of the body and the demands of commerce but the desire for beauty and the hunger for community." Johnson expanded federal government programs for education, poverty, health care, housing, civil rights, and the environment.

Nixon and Civil Rights: "There are those who want instant integration and those who want segregation forever. I believe we need to have a middle course between these two extremes." Nixon worked to delay desegregation in school and prevented extension of the Voting Rights Act.

Carter and the Energy Crisis: "The energy crisis . . . is a problem . . . likely to get progressively worse through the rest of this century. . . . This difficult effort will be the 'moral equivalent of war' . . ." Carter asked Americans to cut back on oil and gas use; passed National Energy Act, which helped reduce U.S. dependence on foreign oil.

Reagan and the Economy: "We're in the worst economic mess since the Great Depression. . . . and the old business-as-usual treatment can't save us." Reagan's new economic plan included budget cuts in social welfare and education programs, tax cuts, and increased defense spending. U.S. national debt almost doubled during his first term.

George Bush and Volunteerism: "I have spoken of a thousand points of light, of all the community organizations . . . doing good." Bush worked to replace some government social programs with volunteer programs.

Clinton and Welfare Reform: Clinton promised to "end the welfare system as we know it." Program put limits on length of time a person could receive welfare benefits and gave money to states to distribute rather than to individuals. Millions moved to new jobs.

PRACTICE

CALIFORNIA CONTENT
STANDARD 11.11.2

Domestic Policy Since World War II

Directions: Choose the letter of the *best* answer.

1 One way Eisenhower showed his belief in the U.S. Constitution was by

A preventing Vice President Nixon from accepting gifts from supporters.

B ordering U.S. troops to invade Korea.

C using federal troops to enforce a Supreme Court decision.

D ending the Truman Doctrine.

2 For President Kennedy, the New Frontier included

A exploring space and helping poor people.

B supporting labor unions and better working conditions.

C spreading democracy and international trade through wars.

D beginning a large aid program to Europe.

3 President Johnson's "Great Society" was

A mostly focused on support for new businesses.

B intended to fight inflation and spur the economy.

C a plan for government to support social programs.

D focused on fighting communism in Vietnam.

4 President Carter proposed the "moral equivalent to war" to combat the problem of

A abuse of the welfare system.

B U.S. dependence on foreign oil.

C drug abuse among teenagers.

D racial problems in large cities.

5 One result of President Reagan's new economic policies was

A a huge increase in international trade.

B an increase in energy conservation.

C a drop in the stock market.

D a sharp rise in the national debt.

6 President Clinton's welfare reform program changed welfare distribution so that money went

A rarely to the elderly.

B directly to the states.

C only to philanthropic organizations.

D primarily to mothers and children.

Name _____   Date _____

The Changing Roles of Women

Specific Objective: Describe the changing roles of women in society as reflected in the entry of more women into the labor force and the changing family structure.

Read the chart to answer the questions on the next page.

Women at Work	Changing Families
• More women work outside the home today than ever—58 percent in 2000 compared to 36 percent in 1960.	• More than 1 of every 3 women (15 years or older) is single (divorced, separated, or never married).
• Nearly as many women (about 61 million) were employed in 2000 as men (about 69 million).	• More than 15 percent of all families are headed by single women (about 6 percent by single men).
• More women are working in nontraditional occupations such as construction and mining, although it is still a small percentage compared to men.	• Women are generally having fewer children.
• In 2000, women earned about 75 percent as much as men for the same work.	• Many more families include a husband and wife who both work outside the home.
• Women hold about half of all management, professional, and related occupations.	• Widespread use of day care allows women (and men) to work and participate in society even while raising children.
• As of 2004, "glass ceiling" (invisible obstacle to advancement to highest levels) is still very strong—only about 7 percent of top-level jobs such as corporate heads or officers are held by women.	• Expectations for women from 1950s and before (women as solely mother and homemaker) not nearly as strong
	• Women's movement of 1960s through today has stressed women's power in society and business as well as equal rights under the law.
• Women-owned businesses have grown rapidly (doubled 1987–2000) and represent the fastest growing sector of the economy.	• Conservative movement of 1980s through today stresses more traditional roles for women and need for women to serve as mothers and homemakers.

Name _____ Date _____

CALIFORNIA CONTENT
STANDARD 11.11.3

The Changing Roles of Women

Directions: Choose the letter of the *best* answer.

1 Which statement *best* describes the number of American women working outside the home in 2000?

A Slightly more than one-third of all women now work outside the home.

B The percentage of women who work outside the home has remained steady since 1960.

C More than half of all women now work outside the home.

D The percentage of women who work outside the home has decreased since 1980.

2 In 2000, women's earnings for the same work as men were

A slightly lower—about 5 percent less than men's.

B significantly lower—about 25 percent less than men's.

C about the same as men's.

D slightly higher because most work in professional jobs.

3 American women in 2004 held only about 7 percent of top-level jobs because

A women are less likely than men to belong to labor unions.

B few women held full-time jobs in large corporations.

C a "glass ceiling" of traditional bias has limited women's advancement.

D women have had fewer years of education than men.

4 The number of businesses owned by American women in recent years has

A stayed about the same since the 1960s.

B decreased slightly because many women's businesses have merged.

C grown slowly because women have not had the money to start them.

D become the fastest growing sector of the economy.

5 Which statement describes *one* change in American families since the 1950s?

A Fewer families have both parents working outside the home.

B More families are headed by single parents.

C More mothers stay at home until their children are in school.

D Families are having more children.

6 *One* reason American women have been able to participate more widely in business and society since 1970 is

A better nutrition that allows women to do more nontraditional jobs.

B the passage of the Equal Rights Amendment.

C the widespread use of day care to provide help with raising children.

D conservative groups who have supported women's rights for many years.

Name _____ Date _____

REVIEW

CALIFORNIA CONTENT
STANDARD 11.11.4

The Constitution and the Watergate Crisis

Specific Objective: Explain the constitutional crisis originating from the Watergate scandal.

Read the sequence diagram to answer the questions on the next page.

The Watergate Burglary

- During the 1972 campaign for president, a Republican group wanted to get an advantage over Democrats by looking at their files and taping their private conversations.
- In June 1972, five men working for Republicans were arrested as they attempted to break into Democratic National Headquarters at the Watergate Hotel in Washington, D.C.

↓

The Cover-up

- Republicans in the Nixon White House, including those involved, denied any knowledge of the attempted burglary.
- Nixon was involved in meetings to ensure the investigation did not involve the White House.
- Documents were shredded and payments made to burglars to remain silent.

↓

The Investigation

- The Senate decided to investigate ties to the White House when a judge made it clear that the burglars probably did not act alone.
- Investigators got evidence of ties to the White House through the burglars and White House staff testimony before the Senate.
- A witness revealed a system that taped all White House conversations.
- Investigators wanted the tapes to clarify people's involvement, including Nixon's.

↓

The Constitutional Crisis

- Nixon had approved a special prosecutor to investigate the incident.
- When the prosecutor took the case to court to get tapes, Nixon ordered him fired.
- The Attorney General and deputy both resigned instead of firing the prosecutor.
- Nixon refused to release the complete tapes. The Senate demanded them.
- Nixon said that the executive branch had a right to keep the tapes for national security.
- The Supreme Court ordered the complete tapes released.
- There was a constitutional conflict over who had the most power—the Supreme Court (judicial branch), Congress (legislative), or Nixon (executive).
- Nixon finally released the tapes, although many had gaps at important times.
- The House Committee voted to impeach Nixon, partially for refusing to release the tapes.
- Nixon resigned in August 1974 before facing an impeachment hearing.

 **PRACTICE**

CALIFORNIA CONTENT
STANDARD 11.11.4

The Constitution and the Watergate Crisis

Directions: Choose the letter of the *best* answer.

'It works!'

Courtesy of Tony Auth

1 What does the cartoon show about the relationship between the Constitution and the Watergate crisis?

A The Constitution had planned for the need to remove a president from office.

B The Constitution included no mention of how to run presidential elections.

C The Constitution supported the ideas of executive privilege and national security.

D Those who wrote the Constitution did not expect it to last for such a long time.

2 The constitutional crisis of Watergate concerned

A the freedom of the press as guaranteed by the First Amendment.

B the balance of power and the system of checks and balances.

C whether the president had the right to tape conversations in the White House.

D whether the legislative branch had the right to impeach the president.

Name _____ Date _____

**CALIFORNIA CONTENT
STANDARD 11.11.5**

The Environmental Movement

Specific Objective: Trace the impact of, need for, and controversies associated with environmental conservation, expansion of the national park system, and the development of environmental protection laws, with particular attention to the interaction between environmental protection advocates and property rights advocates.

Read the summary to answer the questions on the next page.

The Environmental Conservation Movement

- Yellowstone became the first national park in 1872. In 1903, President Theodore Roosevelt established the first federal wildlife refuge. The National Park Service was created in 1916. President Franklin Roosevelt added many historic monuments to the system and made it truly national. The size of the system tripled in the 1990s. Today there are more than 83 million acres under national protection.

- Rachel Carson published *Silent Spring* in 1962. This book warned about the dangers of pesticides. It caused Americans to start thinking more about what they were doing to damage the environment, especially through air and water pollution.

- In the 1970s and 1980s, Congress established the Environmental Protection Agency (EPA) and passed the Clean Air, Clean Water, and Endangered Species acts.

- By the 1990s, Americans had done much to improve the environment. Recycling efforts were common. Government and private groups worked together to protect air, water, forests, and wildlife.

Balancing Environmental Conservation and Economic Growth

- The United States consumes 25 percent of the world's energy, almost all of it in fossil fuels. Debate about how to reduce dependence on foreign oil has led to conflicts over oil exploration in federally protected areas such as the Arctic National Wildlife Refuge.

- Many scientists and public officials are concerned about the potential environmental disasters that could result from global warming. The United States has done little to reduce production of greenhouse gases that cause global warming. It has refused to sign the Kyoto Protocol because of concerns that measures to reduce the gases are too costly and would hurt the economy.

- Some people believe that the limited resources of the earth (especially oil reserves, old growth forests, clean oceans and shorelines) require considerable protection to prevent extreme consequences such as the Exxon Valdez oil spill in Alaska. Critics charge that there is less emphasis on EPA enforcement of environmental laws under President George W. Bush.

- Some property owners believe they should have the right to use their land as they see fit, regardless of larger environmental concerns.

- Some people believe that the need for jobs and economic gains today should outweigh concerns about future environmental problems, such as the loss of endangered species.

Name _____   Date _____

The Environmental Movement

Directions: Choose the letter of the *best* answer.

1 Which statement *best* describes the history of the National Park System?

   A The system tripled in size during the 1990s.

   B Most of the parks were established under Theodore Roosevelt.

   C The biggest additions to the system were made in the 1930s.

   D The system is largely funded by private contributions.

2 Rachel Carson's book, *Silent Spring*, warned Americans about the dangers of

   A acid rain.

   B global warming.

   C nuclear power.

   D pesticide use.

3 The environmental movement in the early 1970s succeeded in

   A reducing American dependence on foreign oil.

   B reducing automobile usage in major cities.

   C establishing the EPA and passing the Clean Air Act.

   D passing restrictions aimed at limiting global warming.

4 Some people in 2004 were concerned about the Arctic National Wildlife Refuge in Alaska because of

   A acid rain from nearby industries.

   B logging operations endangering wildlife.

   C possible oil exploration there.

   D pesticide use by local farmers.

5 Which statement *best* describes U.S. policy concerning global warming?

   A Most U.S. scientists agree that its progress is so slow that it is no longer a problem.

   B The U.S. government has led the way in encouraging other countries to fight global warming.

   C There is widespread agreement by scientists and the U.S. government on how to prevent problems in the future.

   D The United States is concerned that measures to reduce global warming could hurt its economy.

6 Why is it challenging to balance protection of the environment with protection of property rights?

   A because most economic development involves use of the earth's resources

   B because property owners who live in cities have neglected efforts, such as recycling, to protect the environment

   C because environmentalists want all land to be owned by the government

   D because there are no laws to regulate either one

Name _____ Date _____

Poverty and Government Policy

Specific Objective: Analyze the persistence of poverty and how different analyses of this issue influence welfare reform, health insurance reform, and other social policies.

Read the summary to answer the questions on the next page.

History

- Widespread poverty during the Great Depression led to the first government programs to aid the poor. Prosperity after World War II mostly benefited whites who moved from cities to suburbs. Many African Americans and other rural poor moved to cities. Inner cities rapidly became poor and rundown without resources or jobs.

- In the early 1960s, about 20 percent of Americans lived below the poverty line (the minimum needed to meet basic needs of food, clothing and shelter). President Johnson tried to address problems through federal and state training and jobs programs and direct assistance (welfare and food stamps). The effort was known as the *War on Poverty*. Poverty declined to about 11 percent in 1973.

- Economic hard times in the early 1980s caused poverty to rise. Beginning with President Reagan many welfare benefits were cut. President Clinton's program further limited benefits and required poor people to find jobs. President George W. Bush emphasized private charity as a way to help the poor.

Current Poverty Levels

- In 1999, approximately 32.3 million Americans lived below the poverty line. Approximately 15 percent of Americans have no health insurance. The U.S. poverty rate for children is higher than any other industrialized country's. More than 20 percent of African Americans and Hispanics live in poverty compared to about 8 percent of whites. Families headed by single women are hit hardest.

Contrasting Views on Poverty

Society Bears Some Responsibility	Individuals Are Responsible
• Systems in society favor some over others. Racism is a factor. • Education system has failed to give people the tools they need to escape from poverty.	• Society provides opportunities for all to get education and jobs. • Individuals who work hard enough can excel in education and business even if facilities and opportunities are poor.
Effects on Public Policy • Government should provide assistance to those who have fewer opportunities. • Programs to help poor people get better education and jobs are needed. • Adequate health care should be a right of all citizens.	**Effects on Public Policy** • Government should provide incentives to work rather than direct assistance. • Poor people should work harder to get better education and jobs. • Providing health insurance for everyone is too expensive.

Name _____ Date _____

Poverty and Government Policy

_____

Directions: Choose the letter of the *best* answer.

1 Which statement *best* describes poverty in U.S. history?

  A The federal government has always kept a hands-off approach to poverty.

  B In spite of periods of government aid, the problem of poverty persists.

  C Poverty is spread evenly among all racial and ethnic groups.

  D Free public education has allowed all citizens to gain the job skills they need.

2 President Johnson declared the "War on Poverty" because

  A the Vietnam War had just ended and veterans needed help.

  B most of the people who had voted for him were poor.

  C he wanted to keep poverty out of the suburbs.

  D about 20 percent of Americans were living in poverty.

3 How did President Reagan deal with the issue of poverty?

  A He cut welfare benefits as part of his plan to limit government.

  B He offered health insurance to all poor children.

  C He supported affirmative action so poor people could get better jobs.

  D He increased educational assistance for the poor.

4 As a way to help the poor, President George W. Bush advocates that

  A private organizations should provide more assistance.

  B the government is the best resource for providing assistance.

  C cities should offer health insurance to all who can not afford it.

  D federally funded welfare benefits should be more generous.

5 The Americans *most likely* to be poor today are

  A recent immigrants.

  B unemployed white women.

  C rural white families.

  D minorities and children.

6 Which statement *best* describes the belief that led to welfare reform under President Clinton?

  A Poverty has increased, and the government needs to do more to help poor people.

  B As the most prosperous nation, the United States does not have a problem with poverty.

  C The current system fosters dependence on the government rather than self-reliance.

  D If government improves public education everyone should be able to get a good job.

Name _____ Date _____

REVIEW

CALIFORNIA CONTENT
STANDARD 11.11.7

Recent Population and Social Changes

Specific Objective: Explain how the federal, state, and local governments have responded to demographic and social changes such as population shifts to the suburbs, racial concentrations in the cities, Frostbelt-to-Sunbelt migration, international migration, decline of family farms, increases in out-of-wedlock births, and drug abuse.

Read the chart to answer the questions on the next page.

Demographic or Social Change	Government Response
Population shift to the suburbs	• Built interstate highways and state and local roads; increased need for local government services • Policy favored suburban single-family home ownership. • Suburbs provided tax incentives to businesses.
Racial concentration in cities	• Urban renewal projects have had mixed results. • Some local governments have provided economic incentives for minority businesses. • Programs to crack down on crime and drug abuse have often led to discrimination.
Frostbelt-to-Sunbelt Migration	• Spurred by federal defense spending, which created new jobs, funding for interstate highways, and Social Security, which helped retirees move • Tax incentives offered by state and local governments to lure businesses • Some shift in political power in Congress as population has moved South and West
Decline of family farms	• Most federal farm policy favors large corporate farms over small farms. • Government subsidies that encourage the growth of suburbs also speed up the loss of farm land.
Increase in out-of-wedlock births	• In 1996, gave states extra funds as part of welfare reform if they decreased rate of these births • More government emphasis on abstinence instead of birth control
Increase in drug abuse	• Offers prevention programs such as "Just say no" • Recent efforts focused mainly on law enforcement and prosecution; large prison and jail populations as a result

Name _____   Date _____

PRACTICE

CALIFORNIA CONTENT
STANDARD 11.11.7

Recent Population and Social Changes

Directions: Choose the letter of the *best* answer.

1 How did federal government policy support the population shift to the suburbs after World War II?

  A imposed higher taxes on businesses in cities

  B increased support for public transportation

  C located government offices in the suburbs

  D built roads and supporting home ownership

2 A *common* way that state and local governments attract business is through

  A taking control of certain industries.

  B special tax incentives for companies.

  C government programs to train workers.

  D providing better retirement programs.

3 *One* factor in the migration from the Frostbelt to the Sunbelt was

  A federal spending on defense industries that created new jobs.

  B movement of African Americans from rural areas to cities.

  C more liberal welfare policies in the South and West.

  D movement of whites from cities to the suburbs.

4 How have *most* government policies affected family farms?

  A helped small farmers get more profit from food sales

  B did not affect the trend to larger farms

  C helped family farms by encouraging exports

  D added to the decline of family farms

5 *Most* recent government efforts to reduce drug abuse have focused on

  A law enforcement and prosecution.

  B prevention through school and social programs.

  C new types of medical treatment.

  D legalization of some drugs and reduced penalties for others.

6 How did the U.S. government respond to the increase in out-of-wedlock births in the 1980s and 90s?

  A required more birth control programs in schools

  B used welfare reform to reward states that lowered the birthrate among unwed mothers

  C encouraged states to impose criminal penalties on unwed mothers

  D provided more assistance to unwed mothers, so the babies would be well cared for